Common Core
Standards Practice Workbook

Grade 5

Teacher Guide

Glenview, Illinois • Boston, Massachusetts
Chandler, Arizona • Upper Saddle River, New Jersey

ALWAYS LEARNING

PEARSON

ISBN-13: 978-0-328-75695-7
ISBN-10:   0-328-75695-4

1 2 3 4 5 6 7 8 9 10 V069 19 18 17 16 15 14 13

Grade 5 Contents

Standards Practice

Assessment

Teacher Support

About this Guide

Pearson is pleased to offer this **Common Core Standards Practice** Teacher's Guide, a companion to the **Common Core Standards Practice Workbook.** It includes these pages:

- **Common Core Standards Practice pages.** Two pages of practice exercises for each Common Core State Standard. Students will find different kinds of exercises that are similar to the items expected to be on the Next Generation Assessment that students will be taking starting in 2014–2015.

- **Practice for the Common Core Assessment.** Each Practice Assessment consists of one (1) Practice End-of-Year Assessment and two (2) Performance Tasks. One Practice Assessment is found in the Student Workbook, while the second is a "secure" test found only in this Teacher's Guide. The two Practice End-of-Year Assessments are mirror assessments.

  The Practice End-of-Year assessment was built to align to the content emphases of both PARCC and SBAC. That means that 70% of the items assess major content emphases. In addition, many of the items are similar to the innovative items that are expected to be on the upcoming Next Generation Assessments. Students will encounter multiple-response selected-response items; simulated technology-enabled items that ask students to sort answer options into appropriate categories or to construct responses on grids, graphs, and number lines; constructed response items that ask them to explain their reasoning or justify their thinking; and extended constructed response items that include multi-part questions with multi-step solutions. The Performance Tasks present students with problem situations in real-world context and ask students to make use of their developing proficiency with the Standards for Mathematical Practice and their firmer understanding of Math Content to find solutions.

- Answers to all of the student pages as 4-ups.

- **Correlation Chart for the Practice EOY Assessment.** The chart indicates for each item the Content Standard assessed and lessons in *enVisionMATH™ Common Core* and sessions in *Investigations in Number, Data, and Space® for the Common Core* where students can go for more practice of the standard assessed.

- **Scoring Rubrics for the four (4) Performance Tasks.** In additional to recommendations for scoring, these pages list both the Standards for Mathematical Practice and Mathematical Content that the task assesses.

Common Core Standards Practice and Assessments

Name _____

Common Core Standards Practice

5.OA.1 Use parentheses, brackets, or braces in numerical expressions, and evaluate expressions with these symbols.

1. Which expression is equal to 2?

    A $24 \div (2 + 2) \times 5$

    B $(24 \div 2) + (2 \times 5)$

    C $(24 \div 2 + 2) \times 5$

    D $24 \div (2 + 2 \times 5)$

2. Tell whether the equation is true. Justify your answer.

$$2 + 1 \times 5 - 3 \overset{?}{=} (2 + 1) \times (5 - 3)$$

3. Evaluate the expression below.

    $(9 + 2) \times 6 - 5$

4. Evaluate the expression.

    $5 \div (4 - 3) \cdot 3$

5. Evaluate the expression.

    $20 \div (5 \times 2) + 3$

    A 5

    B 9

    C 11

    D 12

6. Which expression is equal to 7?

    A $(5 + 2) \times [6 - (3 + 2)]$

    B $5 + 2 \times 6 - (3 + 2)$

    C $(5 + 2) \times 6 - (3 + 2)$

    D $(5 + 2) \times [6 - (3 \times 2)]$

7. Kevin evaluated the expression below.

$75 - [6(8 - 6) + 3]$

- Step 1: $75 - [6 \cdot 2 + 3]$
- Step 2: $75 - [6 \cdot 5]$
- Step 3: $75 - 30$
- Step 4: 45

The teacher finds an error in Kevin's work.

a. Which step contains the error?

b. Explain the error.

8. Two students simplified the following expression.

Alexandra	**Joe**
$30 \div 2 - 4 \times 3 + 2$	$30 \div 2 - 4 \times 3 + 2$
$= 15 - 4 \times 3 + 2$	$= 15 - 4 \times 3 + 2$
$= 15 - 12 + 2$	$= 15 - 12 + 2$
$= 3 + 2$	$= 15 - 14$
$= 5$	$= 1$

a. Which student simplified the expression correctly?

b. What mistake was made?

Common Core Standards Practice

5.OA.2 Write simple expressions that record calculations with numbers, and interpret numerical expressions without evaluating them.

1. Which expression matches this statement?

   Divide 24 by 6 less than 8.

   A $24 \div (8 - 6)$

   B $24 \div 8 - 6$

   C $(24 \div 6) - 8$

   D $[(24 \div 8) - 6]$

2. Each row in a box of chocolates contains 4 caramels and 8 creams. Which expression represents the number of chocolates in a box with 3 rows of chocolates?

   A $3 + (4 \times 8)$

   B $3 \times (4 + 8)$

   C $(3 \times 4) + (2 \times 8)$

   D $(4 \times 8) \times 3$

3. The price of an adult ticket to the museum is $6.00. The price of a student ticket is $4.00. Write an expression to represent the cost of 4 adult tickets and 8 student tickets.

4. Write an expression to match the statement below.

   Add 5 to 48 divided by 12.

5. Latisha and Raquel ordered two beverages for $1.50 each, two dinners for $12.99 each, and one dessert to share for $3.50. Which expression represents the cost of the meal for each person?

   A $1.50 + 2 \times 12.99 + 3.50 \div 2$

   B $(2 \times 1.50 + 2 \times 12.99 + 3.50) \div 2$

   C $2 \times (1.50 + 12.99 + 3.50)$

   D $(2 \times 1.50 + 12.99) + 3.50 \div 2$

6. Which expression matches the statement below?

   Find the product of 50 minus 5 and 4 divided by 2.

   A $(50 - 5) \times (4 \div 2)$

   B $50 - 5 \times 4 \div 2$

   C $50 \div 5 \times 4 \div 2$

   D $50 - 5 + 4 \div 2$

7. Write an expression to match the statement below.

   Divide the product of 4 and 5 by the sum of 2 and 8.

8. The table below shows the cost of several items sold at The Clothes Shack.

The Clothes Shack	
Item	**Price per article ($)**
Jeans	30
T-Shirt	15
Sweatshirt	20
Caps	10

   Jason went to the Clothes Shack with $150. Write an expression to represent the amount of money Jason has remaining after buying 2 pairs of jeans, 3 T-shirts, and 2 sweatshirts.

Name _____

Common Core Standards Practice

5.OA.3 Generate two numerical patterns using two given rules. Identify apparent relationships between corresponding terms. Form ordered pairs consisting of corresponding terms from the two patterns, and graph the ordered pairs on a coordinate plane.

1. a. Generate two numerical sequences using the rules shown below.

Add 5: 0, _____, _____, _____, _____

Add 20: 0, _____, _____, _____, _____

b. What relationship can you find between the second term in first sequence and the second term in the second sequence?

c. Does this relationship hold for all corresponding terms in the two sequences? Tell how you know.

2. Complete the following table.

Add 8.	8	16			
Subtract 2.	2	4			

3. Ama is emptying a large container of water. The container has 100 gallons of water. Ama opens the valve so that 5 gallons of water flow out each minute.

   a. Complete a table to show how much water flows out of the container over time.

Minutes	0						
Number of gallons	100						

   b. Write ordered pairs for each set of values in the table.

   c. Plot the ordered pairs on the coordinate grid.

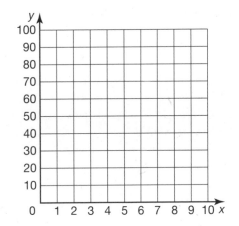

4. a. Write four ordered pairs by applying the rules "subtract 1 from the x-coordinate" and "add 2 to the y-coordinate." Begin at (5,0).

   Ordered Pairs: (5, 0), (____, ____), (____, ____), (____, ____), (____, ____)

   b. Graph the ordered pairs on the grid.

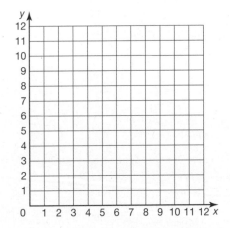

CC 6

Name _____

Common Core Standards Practice

5.NBT.1 Recognize that in a multi-digit number, a digit in one place represents 10 times as much as it represents in the place to its right and $\frac{1}{10}$ of what it represents in the place to its left.

1. How much greater is 500 than 5?

   A 5 times greater

   B 10 times greater

   C 100 times greater

   D 1000 times greater

2. Which describes the relationship between 20,000 and 200,000?

   A 20,000 is 10 times as much as 200,000.

   B 200,000 is $\frac{1}{10}$ of 20,000.

   C 20,000 is $\frac{1}{100}$ of 200,000.

   D 20,000 is $\frac{1}{10}$ of 200,000.

3. How is the value of 2 in the number 542 different from the value of 2 in the number 324?

4. How is the value of 4 in 864 related to the value of 4 in 846?

5. How much greater is 300 than 3?

    A 10 times

    B 100 times

    C 1,000 times

    D 10,000 times

6. What is the relationship between 5,000 and 500,000?

    A 5,000 is $\frac{1}{10}$ the value of 500,000.

    B 5,000 is $\frac{1}{100}$ the value of 500,000.

    C 5,000 is 100 times the value of 500,000.

    D 5,000 is 10 times the value of 500,000.

7. What is the difference in place value between the 2 in 324 and the 2 in 0.324?

8. The total number of people who visited the Ocean Adventure Park last year was 7,040,836. What is the value of the digit 4 in this number?

9. How many tenths are in 13.58?

10. How many hundredths are in 401.308?

Name _____

Common Core Standards Practice

5.NBT.2 Explain patterns in the number of zeros of the product when multiplying a number by powers of 10, and explain patterns in the placement of the decimal point when a decimal is multiplied or divided by a power of 10. Use whole-number exponents to denote powers of 10.

1. Circle all of the expressions that equal 372,000.

372×10^3 3.72×10^6 372×10^4

37.2×10^4 37.2×10^3 3.72×10^5

2. Complete the table.

Expression	Product
5×10^1	50
5×10^2	
5×10^3	
5×10^4	

What pattern do you observe in the table?

3. Complete the table.

Expression	Quotient
$76 \div 10^1$	7.6
$76 \div 10^2$	
$76 \div 10^3$	
$76 \div 10^4$	

What pattern do you observe in the table?

CC 9

4. Draw a model to show the value of this expression.

$5 \div 10^2$

5. Match the numbers on the left with an equivalent expression on the right. Some may have more than one equivalent expression. Some may have no equivalent expressions.

0.67 $1067 \div 10^2$

                                  $4.239 \div 10^3$

10.67 $67 \div 10^3$

                                  1.067×10^1

4,239 $67 \div 10^2$

                                  4.239×10^3

6. Circle all of the expressions that are equivalent to 1,795,000.

$1,795 \times 10^3$ 17.95×10^5 1.795×10^7

179.5×10^5 17.95×10^6 $1,795 \times 10^3$

Name _____

Common Core Standards Practice

5.NBT.3a Read, write, and compare decimals to thousandths. Read and write decimals to thousandths using base-ten numerals, number names, and expanded form.

1. Sharon is writing 4.072 in expanded form. What number makes the equation true?

   4.072 = 4 + 0.0 + _____ + 0.002

   A 7
   B 0.7
   C 0.07
   D 0.007

2. What is the standard form of the number below?

   10 + 1 + 0.9 + 0.02 + 0.003

   A 1192.3
   B 119.23
   C 1.1923
   D 11.923

3. Jeremy has a batting average of 0.235. What is the batting average written in expanded form?

4. Match these numbers with their expanded forms.

   3.6

   $4 \times 10 + 1 \times \frac{1}{10} + 5 \times \frac{1}{100}$

   3.06

   $3 \times 1 + 6 \times \frac{1}{100}$

   40.15

   $3 \times 1 + 6 \times \frac{1}{10}$

   4,015

   $4 \times 1000 + 1 \times 10 + 5 \times 1$

CC11

5. Which show different forms of 5.39? Circle all that are equal to 5.39.

    A Five and thirty-nine hundredths

    B $539 \div 10^2$

    C $5 + 0.3 + 0.09$

    D 5 and 39 tenths

    E 0.539×10^2

    F 0.539×10^1

6. What is the expanded form of five and six hundred fourteen thousandths?

    A $5 + 0.6 + 0.01 + 0.004$

    B $5 + 0.06 + 0.01 + 0.004$

    C $5 + 0.06 + 0.001 + 0.004$

    D $5 + 0.6 + 0.001 + 0.0004$

7. Write these expressions in standard form.

    a. $(4 \times 1) + \left(6 \times \frac{1}{10}\right)$

    b. $4 \times 10 + 3 \times \frac{1}{10} + 7 \times \frac{1}{100} + 5 \times \frac{1}{1000}$

    c. $(9 \times 10) + \left(5 \times \frac{1}{10}\right)$

    d. $(9 \times 1) + \left(5 \times \frac{1}{100}\right)$

Name _____

Common Core Standards Practice

5.NBT.3b Read, write, and compare decimals to thousandths. Compare two decimals to thousandths based on meanings of the digits in each place, using >, =, and < symbols to record the results of comparisons.

1. Which of the following numbers is greater than 7.03?

    A 7.031

    B 7.030

    C 7.003

    D 7.0

Explain how you know.

2. Which of the following lists three decimals between 8.6 and 9.2?

    A eight and seven tenths, 8.61, 8.5

    B eight and seven hundredths, 9.1, 9.0

    C eight and eight tenths, 9.21, 9.01

    D eight and seventy-five hundredths, 8.80, 9.19

3. The length of New York's subway is 368 km, while the length of Moscow's subway is 306.2 km. Which subway system is longer? Use >, <, or = to compare the two lengths. Then justify your answer using place value.

4. In each box, write <, >, or = to make a true sentence:

    a. 46.491 ☐ 46.577   **b.** 2.15 ☐ 2.150   **c.** 11.341 ☐ 11.34

    d. 0.495 ☐ 0.503   **e.** 0.080 ☐ 0.08   **f.** 8.70 ☐ 8.697

CC 13

5. Matt completed his first race in 15.163 seconds. The time of his second race was 15.24 seconds. Which of the following shows the correct relationship between 15.163 and 15.24?

A $15.163 < 15.24$

B $15.163 > 15.24$

C $15.24 < 15.163$

D $15.24 = 15.163$

Justify your answer.

6. Which of the following numbers is less than 23.90?

A 23.9

B 23.09

C 23.91

D 23.92

7. Mrs Sanders bought 2 pumpkins. The first one weighed 4.89 kilograms; the second one weighed 4.9 kilograms. Use $>$, $<$, or $=$ to compare the weights.

Justify your answer.

8. Wendy, Todd, and Theresa went on a hike. They hiked 7.25 miles, 7.5 miles, and 7.245 miles. Order the distances from least to greatest.

Justify your answer using place value.

Name _____

Common Core Standards Practice

5.NBT.4 Use place value understanding to round decimals to any place.

1. What is 5.385 rounded to the nearest tenth?

   A 5.3

   B 5.4

   C 5.5

   D 5.6

2. What is 4.62 rounded to the nearest whole number?

   A 5

   B 4.5

   C 4.7

   D 4.5

3. Round these numbers to the nearest tenth.

   a. 182.886   d. 7.96

   b. 0.459   e. 0.3

   c. 4.06   f. 3.21

4. Round these numbers to the nearest hundredth.

   a. 182.886   d. 8.31

   b. 0.459   e. 8.072

   c. 0.172   f. 130.039

CC 15

5. Which of these numbers, when rounded to the nearest hundredth, is 0.05? Circle all that round to 0.05.

0.049   0.057   0.052   0.44   0.55

6. What is 45.0189 rounded to the nearest thousandth?

A 45.018

B 45.0188

C 45.019

D 45.0289

7. What is 4.106 rounded to the nearest hundredth?

A 4.10

B 4.11

C 4.12

D 4.107

8. A box of uncooked spaghetti costs $0.1369 per ounce. How much is this cost to the nearest cent?

9. Roberto's baseball batting average is 0.278. What is his batting average rounded to the nearest hundredth?

10. Which of these numbers, when rounded to the nearest tenth, is 8.3? Circle all that round to 8.3.

8.28   8.24   8.33   8.36   8.25

Name _____

Common Core Standards Practice

5.NBT.5 Fluently multiply multi-digit whole numbers using the standard algorithm.

Find these products.

1.   42
       $\times$ 27

2.   632
       $\times$ 49

3.   38
       $\times$ 87

4.   155
       $\times$ 23

5.   76
       $\times$ 17

6.   41
       $\times$ 86

7.   138
       $\times$ 57

8.   209
       $\times$ 54

Find these products.

9. $\begin{array}{r} 19 \\ \times\ 87 \\ \hline \end{array}$

10. $\begin{array}{r} 397 \\ \times\ 53 \\ \hline \end{array}$

11. $\begin{array}{r} 441 \\ \times\ 63 \\ \hline \end{array}$

12. $\begin{array}{r} 445 \\ \times\ 273 \\ \hline \end{array}$

13. $\begin{array}{r} 632 \\ \times\ 56 \\ \hline \end{array}$

14. $\begin{array}{r} 518 \\ \times\ 107 \\ \hline \end{array}$

15. $\begin{array}{r} 479 \\ \times\ 328 \\ \hline \end{array}$

16. $\begin{array}{r} 169 \\ \times\ 304 \\ \hline \end{array}$

Name _____

Common Core Standards Practice

5.NBT.6 Find whole-number quotients of whole numbers with up to four-digit dividends and two-digit divisors, using strategies based on place value, the properties of operations, and/or the relationship between multiplication and division. Illustrate and explain the calculation by using equations, rectangular arrays, and/or area models.

Solve these division problems.

1. $97\overline{)2,134}$

2. $69\overline{)2,898}$

3. A theater has 182 seats that are divided evenly into 14 rows. How many seats are in each row?

    a. Draw a model of the problem and write an equation that describes the model.

    b. Solve the equation you wrote.

4. Neil has 1,216 sports cards that he divides into 32 packages, each with the same number of cards. How many cards are in each package?

    a. Draw a model that represents this probem, and write an equation to match the model.

    b. Solve the equation you wrote.

Solve these division problems.

5. $68 \overline{)1,904}$

6. $57 \overline{)5,415}$

7. Marcia has 1,792 flowers for making centerpieces. Each centerpiece will have 64 flowers. How many centerpieces can she make?

   a. Draw a simple model that explains this probem, and write an equation that describes the model.

   b. Solve the equation you wrote.

8. A plant nursery will plant 1,560 trees in ten different plots of land. Each plot of land will have the same number of trees, planted in rows of 12.

   a. How many trees will be planted in each plot of land?

   b. How many rows of trees will be on each plot of land?

   c. Justify your solutions using equations or models.

CC 20

Name _____

Common Core Standards Practice

5.NBT.7 Add, subtract, multiply, and divide decimals to hundredths, using concrete models or drawings and strategies based on place value, properties of operations, and/or the relationship between addition and subtraction; relate the strategy to a written method and explain the reasoning used.

1. The temperature increased from 58.7°F to 92.6°F. Find the difference between the two temperatures in degrees Fahrenheit.

2. The table shows the mass of four packages. What is the total mass of the packages?

Package	Mass (kg)
1	3.94
2	14.81
3	11.27
4	7.65

3. Alexandra went to the mall on Saturday and bought the items listed in the table. She bought each item at the discount price.

Item	Original Price ($)	Discount Price ($)
Bracelet	25.75	19.50
Hat	19.25	15.00

   a. What is the total cost of the items at their original prices?

   b. How much did Alexandra save?

   c. Explain how you determined how much she saved.

4. A car gets 28.45 miles on 1 gallon of gasoline. The gasoline tank holds 11.5 gallons.

    a. Describe how to find how far the driver can drive the car on a full tank of gasoline.

    b. How far can the driver go in this car on a full tank?

5. Three stores sell Cactus Cola. The stores sell the same bottles, but they group them in packs of either 6, 12, or 24 bottles.

Store A	6-pack	$3.45
Store B	12-pack	$5.25
Store C	24-pack	$10.99

    a. How can you tell which store sells a bottle of cola for the lowest price?

    b. Which store sells Cactus cola bottles for the lowest price? What is this price?

6. The table shows the admission price to a zoo.

Adult	$7.45
Student	$4.50
Child under 5	$3.75

The Chung family buys 2 adult tickets, 2 student tickets, and 1 child's ticket. What is the total cost of the tickets?

Name _____

Common Core Standards Practice

5.NF.1 Add and subtract fractions with unlike denominators (including mixed numbers) by replacing given fractions with equivalent fractions in such a way as to produce an equivalent sum or difference of fractions with like denominators.

1. Which of these is equal to the sum of $\frac{4}{6}$ and $\frac{4}{9}$? Circle all that are equal to the sum.

   $\frac{10}{9}$ $\qquad$ $\frac{8}{15}$ $\qquad$ $\frac{40}{36}$ $\qquad$ $\frac{4}{15}$ $\qquad$ $\frac{11}{7}$ $\qquad$ $1\frac{2}{18}$

2. Which of these is equal to the difference of $\frac{8}{9}$ and $\frac{2}{3}$? Circle all that are equal to the difference.

   $\frac{1}{12}$ $\qquad$ $\frac{2}{9}$ $\qquad$ $\frac{9}{14}$ $\qquad$ $\frac{1}{9}$ $\qquad$ $\frac{4}{18}$ $\qquad$ $1\frac{5}{9}$

3. Which equivalent fractions can you use to find the sum of $\frac{2}{8} + \frac{3}{9}$?

4. Find the sum.

   $\frac{2}{8} + \frac{3}{9}$

5. Which equivalent fractions can you use to find the difference of $5\frac{3}{12}$ and $1\frac{4}{9}$?

6. Find the difference.

   $5\frac{3}{12} - 1\frac{4}{9}$

CC 23

7. Place these expressions in the appropriate column.

Less than 1	Equal to 1	Greater than 1

$$\frac{1}{5} + \frac{3}{12} \qquad 3\frac{1}{4} - 2\frac{1}{2} \qquad \frac{7}{12} + \frac{2}{3} \qquad 3\frac{1}{3} - 1\frac{5}{6}$$

$$1\frac{1}{4} - \frac{9}{12} \qquad \frac{3}{12} + \frac{3}{4} \qquad 1\frac{4}{18} - \frac{2}{9} \qquad \frac{1}{2} + \frac{5}{8}$$

8. Which equivalent fractions can you use to find the sum of $2\frac{5}{6} + 1\frac{3}{4}$?

9. Find the sum.

$$2\frac{5}{6} + 1\frac{3}{4}$$

10. Which equivalent fractions can you use to find the difference of $2\frac{5}{6}$ and $\frac{9}{5}$?

11. Find the difference.

$$2\frac{5}{6} - \frac{9}{5}$$

5

Name _____

Common Core Standards Practice

5.NF.2 Solve word problems involving addition and subtraction of fractions referring to the same whole, including cases of unlike denominators, e.g., by using visual fraction models or equations to represent the problem. Use benchmark fractions and number sense of fractions to estimate mentally and assess the reasonableness of answers.

1. Alex practices his guitar $\frac{5}{8}$ of an hour on Wednesday and $3\frac{3}{4}$ hours on Thursday.

    a. Write an equation that can be used to determine how many hours Alex practiced his guitar on Wednesday and Thursday.

    b. Solve the equation you wrote.

2. Anna used $\frac{2}{5}$ yard of ribbon for one craft project and $\frac{3}{4}$ yard of ribbon for a second craft project.

    a. Estimate how much ribbon Anna used for the two projects.

    b. Use the number line to model the problem situation.

    c. How much ribbon did Anna use for the two craft projects?

3. Maria bought $1\frac{1}{2}$ pounds of nails for a carpentry project. She ended up with $\frac{3}{8}$ pound of nails when she finished the project.

   a. Write an equation that can be used to determine how much of the $1\frac{1}{2}$ pounds of nails Maria used.

   b. Solve the equation you wrote.

4. Jack ran $\frac{2}{8}$ mile and Roy ran $\frac{2}{3}$ mile.

   a. What benchmark fractions can be used to estimate how much farther Roy ran than Jack?

   b. Using the benchmark fractions, what is a reasonable estimate for the difference between the two distances?

   c. What is the actual difference?

5. Eva's new dog weighed $5\frac{7}{8}$ pounds when she first got him 4 weeks ago. Now he weighs $12\frac{1}{4}$ pounds.

   a. Eva thinks that her dog has gained 6 pounds since she got him. Is her estimate reasonable?

   b. How much weight has Eva's dog actually gained?

CC 26

Name _____

Common Core Standards Practice

5.NF.3 Interpret a fraction as division of the numerator by the denominator ($\frac{a}{b} = a \div b$). Solve word problems involving division of whole numbers leading to answers in the form of fractions or mixed numbers, e.g., by using visual fraction models or equations to represent the problem.

1. Which division expression matches the model?

   A $3 \div 4$ **C** $3 \div 2$

   B $2 \div 3$ **D** $4 \div 2$

2. Which model matches the division expression?

$6 \div 4$

3. a. Use the bar model below to show 8 bars divided evenly into 5 parts.

   b. Is each part bigger or smaller than the individual bars? Explain how you know.

4. a. Use the bar model below to show 5 bars divided evenly into 8 parts.

   b. Is each part bigger or smaller than the individual bars? Explain how you know.

5. Eva has 35 apples. She divides them equally into 7 bags. Which fraction represents the number of apples Eva puts in each bag?

  A $\frac{35}{7}$

  B $\frac{7}{35}$

  C $\frac{35}{5}$

  D $\frac{28}{35}$

6. Beth has 8 acres of land. She wants to grow 5 types of crops, each on the same size plot.

  a. Write a division statement to represent the number of acres of land for each crop.

  b. Write your answer as a mixed number.

7. Ms. George baked 2 cakes of equal size. Each of her 12 guests ate the same amount of cake, and no cake was left over.

  a. What fraction of a cake did each guest eat?

  b. How do you think Ms. George cut the cakes into equal pieces? Explain.

8. Allen bought a 15-pound bag of ice. He distributed the ice evenly among 4 coolers. How many pounds of ice went into each cooler? Express your answer as a mixed number.

Name _____

Common Core Standards Practice

5.NF.4a Apply and extend previous understandings of multiplication to multiply a fraction or whole number by a fraction. Interpret the product $(\frac{a}{b}) \times q$ as a parts of a partition of q into b equal parts; equivalently, as the result of a sequence of operations $a \times q \div b$.

1. A baker uses $\frac{2}{3}$ of a stick of butter to make one batch of cookies. How many sticks of butter does she need to make 3 batches of cookies?

    a. The model below represents the problem situation. Explain the model.

    b. What does each shaded part represent?

    c. How many shaded parts are in the model?

    d. Write an expression that can be used to determine how many sticks of butter the baker needs.

    e. How much butter does the baker need for three batches of cookies?

2. Use the model below to show $\frac{2}{5} \times 4$.

3. Explain why $2 \times \frac{3}{8}$ is equivalent to $2 \times 3 \times \frac{1}{8}$.

4. Match the model with the expression.

$\frac{2}{9} \times 3$

$4 \times \frac{1}{3}$

$\frac{3}{4} \times 2$

$5 \times \frac{1}{2}$

5. Draw a model to show $\frac{1}{4} \times \frac{2}{3}$. Then find the product.

6. Draw a model to show $5 \times \frac{4}{5}$. Then find the product.

Name _____

Common Core Standards Practice

5.NF.4b Apply and extend previous understandings of multiplication to multiply a fraction or whole number by a fraction. Find the area of a rectangle with fractional side lengths by tiling it with unit squares of the appropriate unit fraction side lengths, and show that the area is the same as would be found by multiplying the side lengths. Multiply fractional side lengths to find areas of rectangles, and represent fraction products as rectangular areas.

For 1–4, write an equation to find the area of the shaded rectangles. Then solve the equation.

1.

2.

3.

4.

5. Angie got a new area rug for her room. The figure on the right shows the dimensions of her room and the area rug.

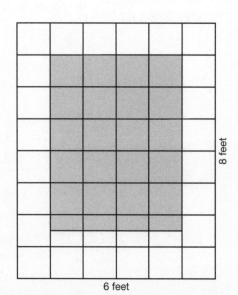

   a. What are the dimensions of the area rug?

   Width: _____

   Length: _____

   b. What is the area of the area rug?

CC 31

6. What is the area of a rectangle with length 5 feet and width $6\frac{1}{2}$ feet?

A 30 ft²

B $30\frac{1}{2}$ ft²

C $34\frac{1}{2}$ ft²

D $32\frac{1}{2}$ ft²

7. What is the area of a rectangle that is $8\frac{2}{5}$ inches long and 6 inches wide?

A $5\frac{2}{5}$ in.²

B $48\frac{2}{5}$ in.²

C $50\frac{2}{5}$ in.²

D $100\frac{4}{5}$ in.²

8. Find the area of a rectangle that is $6\frac{1}{3}$ inches long and $4\frac{3}{4}$ inches wide.

9. Jay arranges 18 feet of fencing into a rectangle that is 5 feet long and 4 feet wide. Show that he could make a larger area by arranging the fencing into a square.

10. John has a rectangular patio that is $6\frac{3}{4}$ yards long and $4\frac{1}{3}$ yards wide. What is the area of the patio?

Name _____

Common Core Standards Practice

5.NF.5a Interpret multiplication as scaling (resizing) by: Comparing the size of a product to the size of one factor on the basis of the size of the other factor, without performing the indicated multiplication.

1. Write the expressions in the appropriate place. You should NOT find the products of the expressions.

Less than 5	Equal to 5	Greater than 5

$5 \times \dfrac{3}{2}$ $\qquad$ $5 \times \dfrac{2}{3}$ $\qquad$ $5 \times \dfrac{4}{3}$ $\qquad$ $\dfrac{1}{2} \times 10$

$\dfrac{1}{2} \times 5$ $\qquad$ $\dfrac{3}{3} \times 5$ $\qquad$ $\dfrac{7}{8} \times 5$ $\qquad$ $5 \times \dfrac{4}{4}$

2. For each statement 2a through 2d, circle YES if the statement is true or NO if the statement is not true.

   a. $\dfrac{3}{5} \times 5 > 5$ $\qquad$ YES $\qquad$ NO

   b. $\dfrac{3}{5} \times 5 > \dfrac{3}{5}$ $\qquad$ YES $\qquad$ NO

   c. $6 \times \dfrac{3}{2} > 6$ $\qquad$ YES $\qquad$ NO

   d. $6 \times \dfrac{3}{2} < \dfrac{3}{2}$ $\qquad$ YES $\qquad$ NO

3. Jeff feeds the family dog on Wednesdays and his sister Melody feeds the dog on Fridays. On Wednesday, Jeff gave the dog $\frac{5}{8}$ of an 8-ounce can of dog food. On Friday, Melody, gave the dog $\frac{1}{2}$ of an 8-ounce can of dog food.

   a. Write an expression that can be use to determine how many ounces of dog food Jeff fed the dog on Wednesday.

   b. Write an expression that can be use to determine how many ounces of dog food Melody fed the dog on Friday.

   c. Who gave the dog more food, Jeff or Melody? Explain your answer.

4. For each statement 4a through 4d, circle YES if the statement is true or NO if the statement is not true.

   a. $\frac{5}{2} \times 3 > 3$ YES   NO

   b. $\frac{5}{2} \times 3 < \frac{5}{2}$ YES   NO

   c. $10 \times \frac{4}{5} < 10$ YES   NO

   d. $10 \times \frac{4}{5} > \frac{4}{5}$ YES   NO

5. For each pair of expressions, circle the greater product without finding the product.

   a. $\frac{3}{4} \times \frac{2}{3}$ and $\frac{3}{4} \times \frac{1}{2}$

   b. $\frac{2}{3} \times 3\frac{1}{4}$ and $\frac{4}{3} \times 3\frac{1}{4}$

   c. $\frac{3}{8} \times \frac{3}{8}$ and $\frac{3}{8} \times \frac{1}{2}$

Name _____

Common Core Standards Practice

5.NF.5b Interpret multiplication as scaling (resizing) by: Explaining why multiplying a given number by a fraction greater than 1 results in a product greater than the given number (recognizing multiplication by whole numbers greater than 1 as a familiar case); explaining why multiplying a given number by a fraction less than 1 results in a product smaller than the given number; and relating the principle of fraction equivalence $\frac{a}{b} = \frac{(n \times a)}{(n \times b)}$ to the effect of multiplying $\frac{a}{b}$ by 1.

1. Sam buys two carpets. One carpet is 3 feet by $\frac{7}{8}$ foot. The other carpet is 3 feet by $\frac{3}{4}$ foot.

   a. Which carpet has the greater area? Explain how you can find the answer without calculating either area.

   b. Which carpet has an area less than 3 square feet? How do you know?

2. Jasmine tapes together 3 straws in a straight line. Each straw is $9\frac{1}{2}$ inches long. To find the total length of the straws, Jasmine multiplies $9\frac{1}{2}$ by $\frac{3}{3}$.

   a. Describe the error Jasmine made.

   b. What is the value of the product that Jasmine found? Explain.

3. Explain why the product of 9 and $\frac{2}{3}$ is less than 9.

4. The model shows three equal mixed numbers.

    a. Write the product that the model represents.

    b. How does the model show that the product is greater than 8?

5. Explain why the product of 12 and $\frac{3}{2}$ is greater than 12.

6. The equation shows two equivalent fractions.

$$\frac{8 \times \text{?}}{10 \times \text{?}} = \frac{48}{60}$$

    a. What is the value of the question mark in the equation?

    b. How do you know that $\frac{8}{10}$ and $\frac{48}{60}$ are equivalent?

    c. Write another fraction that is equal to $\frac{8}{10}$.

Name _____

Common Core Standards Practice

5.NF.6 Solve real world problems involving multiplication of fractions and mixed numbers, e.g., by using visual fraction models or equations to represent the problem.

1. Mato's marinara recipe calls for $\frac{3}{4}$ tablespoon of tomato paste. He plans to make 12 batches of marinara. How much tomato paste will Mato need?

    a. Draw a model to represent the problem situation. Then find the solution.

2. John is training for a bicycle race. This week he rode his bicycle a total of 13 miles. Next week he plans to ride $2\frac{1}{2}$ times as far. How many miles will John ride his bicycle next week? Write an equation to represent the problem situation. Then solve the equation.

3. It snowed $37\frac{3}{4}$ inches last winter, which was 2 times more snow than the average. What is the average snow fall?

    a. Write an equation that matches the problem situation. Then solve the equation.

4. Alan's cake recipe requires $3\frac{2}{3}$ cups of flour. Alan is making 6 cakes. How much flour does he need?

    a. Draw a model to represent the problem situation.

    b. Write an equation to match the model you drew. Then solve the equation.

5. Julia and Awan are making a retangular banner. The banner will be $4\frac{1}{4}$ feet by $2\frac{3}{4}$ feet. What will be the area of the banner?

Name _____

Common Core Standards Practice

5.NF.7a Apply and extend previous understandings of division to divide unit fractions by whole numbers and whole numbers by unit fractions. Interpret division of a unit fraction by a non-zero whole number, and compute such quotients.

1. Five friends will share equally $\frac{1}{2}$ yard of felt for an art project. How much felt will each friend get?

   a. Use the model to represent the problem situation.

   b. Describe in words what the model shows.

   c. Write and solve an equation that matches the model.

2. A farmer will divide a $\frac{1}{4}$-acre plot of land into three equal-sized sections. What will be the size of each section?

   a. Use the model to represent the problem situation.

   b. Describe in words what the model shows.

   c. Write and solve an equation that matches the model.

CC 39

3. Which of these models show $\frac{1}{5} \div 6$? Circle all that apply.

4. a. Describe a problem situation to match the equation below.

$$\frac{1}{3} \div 7 = \square$$

b. Draw a model to represent the problem situation.

c. Write and solve an equation that matches the model.

Name _____

Common Core Standards Practice

5.NF.7b Apply and extend previous understandings of division to divide unit fractions by whole numbers and whole numbers by unit fractions. Interpret division of a whole number by a unit fraction, and compute such quotients.

1. How many $\frac{1}{2}$-pound pieces are in a 3-pound piece of cheese?

   a. Complete the model to represent the problem situation.

                       1 lb   2 lb   3 lb

   b. Describe in words what the model shows.

   c. Write and solve an equation to match the model.

2. How many $\frac{1}{4}$-mile segments are in a 2-mile relay?

   a. Complete the model to represent the problem situation.

        0   1   2

   b. Describe in words what the model shows.

   c. Write and solve an equation that matches the model.

CC 41

3. a. Describe a problem situation that matches this model.

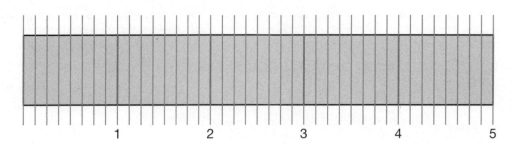

b. Write and solve an equation to match the model.

4. Match the model to the expression. Not all expressions match a model. Not all models match an expression.

$4 \div \frac{1}{4}$

$2 \div \frac{1}{6}$

$6 \div \frac{1}{3}$

$5 \div \frac{1}{2}$

Name _____

Common Core Standards Practice

5.NF.7c Apply and extend previous understandings of division to divide unit fractions by whole numbers and whole numbers by unit fractions. Solve real world problems involving division of unit fractions by non-zero whole numbers and division of whole numbers by unit fractions, e.g., by using visual fraction models and equations to represent the problem.

1. Jimmy buys 3 whole pizzas. Each slice is $\frac{1}{8}$ of a pizza. How many slices are in all 3 pizzas?

   A 24

   B $\frac{1}{24}$

   C 32

   D $\frac{1}{32}$

2. Jack buys a bag of 5 apples, each equal in size. He eats $\frac{1}{2}$ of one apple. What fraction of the bag of apples did he eat?

   A 5

   B $\frac{1}{10}$

   C $\frac{1}{2}$

   D $\frac{2}{5}$

3. Jonny uses $\frac{1}{5}$ of a jar of dressing on 4 servings of salad. He uses an equal amount of dressing on each serving.

   a. Write an equation that can be used to determine the fraction of the jar of dressing that he uses on each serving.

   b. Solve the equation you wrote.

4. Debbi spent a total of 6 hours decorating her classroom. She worked in sessions that each lasted $\frac{1}{3}$ hour.

   a. Write an equation that can be used to determine how many sessions Debbi needed.

   b. Solve the equation you wrote.

5. Barry buys a plot of land that measures $\frac{1}{2}$ acre. He divides the plot into 5 equal pieces.

    a. Draw a model to illustrate the problem.

    b. What fraction of an acre is each piece?

6. A turtle walks at an average speed of $\frac{1}{3}$ mile per hour.

    a. Write an equation that can be used to find how long it would take the turtle to walk 2 miles.

    b. Solve the equation you wrote.

7. Mr. Smith has 7 cups of raisins. He likes to add $\frac{1}{4}$ cup of raisins to a bowl of cereal.

    a. Write an equation that can be used to determine how many bowls of cereal Mr. Smith can supply with raisins.

    b. Solve the equation you wrote.

8. a. Draw a model to illustrate the division problem $\frac{1}{5} \div 3$.

    b. Find the quotient.

Name _____

Common Core Standards Practice

5.MD.1 Convert among different-sized standard measurement units within a given measurement system (e.g., convert 5 cm to 0.05 m), and use these conversions in solving multi-step, real world problems.

1. How many kilometers equal 1,200 meters?

   A 0.12

   B 1.2

   C 12

   D 120

2. How many pints are in 5.5 gallons?

   A 22

   B 33

   C 44

   D 55

3. Polly measures the height of a bookcase to be 2 feet, 10 inches.

   a. What is the height of the bookcase in inches?

   b. Is the height of the bookcase less than, equal to, or greater than 1 yard? Explain how you know.

4. Carl ran 120 feet, while his friend Eva ran 25 yards.

   a. Express 25 yards in feet.

   b. Express 120 feet in yards.

5. Which measurements are equal to 12 feet? Circle all that apply.

60 inches   4 yards   108 inches   3 yards

2 yards   120 inches   6 yards   144 inches

6. Which measurements are equal to 66 meters? Circle all that apply.

330 cm   3,300 cm   33,000 mm   0.33 km

0.66 km   6,600 cm   660 cm   66,000 mm

7. Jan's puppy has a mass of 3.9 kg. Alice's puppy has a mass of 2,750 g.

    a. Write the mass of Alice's puppy in kilograms.

    b. Whose puppy has a greater mass? Explain how you know.

8. Mike buys 4.5 meters of ribbon for a party.

    a. What is the length of the ribbon in centimeters?

    b. What is the length of the ribbon in millimeters?

Name _____

Common Core Standards Practice

5.MD.2 Make a line plot to display a data set of measurements in fractions of a unit ($\frac{1}{2}$, $\frac{1}{4}$, $\frac{1}{8}$). Use operations on fractions for this grade to solve problems involving information presented in line plots.

A teacher asked students to write the total number of hours that they each spent studying math and doing math homework in the last week. She recorded the data in a table.

Hours Spent on Math Last Week

$1\frac{1}{2}$	$1\frac{3}{4}$	$1\frac{1}{4}$	$2\frac{1}{4}$	$3\frac{1}{4}$	$\frac{3}{4}$	$2\frac{1}{2}$	$3\frac{3}{4}$	$5\frac{1}{4}$	$3\frac{1}{2}$	$4\frac{1}{4}$	$2\frac{1}{4}$
$3\frac{1}{2}$	$2\frac{3}{4}$	$2\frac{1}{2}$	$4\frac{3}{4}$	$3\frac{1}{2}$	$2\frac{1}{4}$	$3\frac{1}{4}$	$2\frac{3}{4}$	$2\frac{1}{4}$	$1\frac{3}{4}$	$3\frac{3}{4}$	$3\frac{1}{2}$

1. Make a line plot of this data.

2. How much longer was the greatest amount of time spent than the least amount of time spent on math last week?

3. How many times greater was the greatest amount of time spent than the least amount of time spent on math last week?

4. What were the two most common number of hours spent on math last week? What is the difference between those times?

CC 47

The students in two fifth grade classes recorded the number of miles they walked for the charity walk.

Miles Walked

2	$1\frac{3}{4}$	$2\frac{3}{4}$	$2\frac{1}{4}$	3	$3\frac{1}{4}$	$3\frac{1}{2}$	$3\frac{3}{4}$	4	$4\frac{1}{4}$	$4\frac{1}{2}$	$2\frac{1}{4}$
$6\frac{1}{2}$	$6\frac{1}{4}$	$3\frac{1}{2}$	4	$4\frac{1}{2}$	$4\frac{1}{4}$	$5\frac{1}{2}$	$4\frac{1}{4}$	6	3	$3\frac{3}{4}$	4
$4\frac{1}{4}$	$5\frac{1}{2}$	5	4	$3\frac{1}{2}$	$4\frac{1}{4}$	6	8	$5\frac{3}{4}$	$7\frac{1}{2}$	$5\frac{1}{2}$	$7\frac{1}{4}$

5. Make a line plot of the data.

6. What was the greatest difference between the number of miles walked by any two students?

7. Of the group of students who each walked $4\frac{1}{4}$ miles, how many miles did they walk in all?

8. Lisa and Jorge walked the second and third most miles. How many miles did Lisa and Jorge walk combined?

Name _____

Common Core Standards Practice

5.MD.3ab Recognize volume as an attribute of solid figures and understand concepts of volume measurement. A cube with side length 1 unit, called a "unit cube," is said to have "one cubic unit" of volume, and can be used to measure volume. A solid figure which can be packed without gaps or overlaps using n unit cubes is said to have a volume of n cubic units.

1. Which of these describes a measure of volume? Circle all that apply.

   the height of a wall   the number of tiles that cover a floor

   the distance around a yard   the number of packing peanuts in a box

   the amount of crushed rock   the amount of yard a garden takes up
   that fills a hole

2. Janelle has a large supply of small cubes, each the same size. How could she use the cubes to measure the volume of a shoebox?

3. Bill arranges 50 small cubes in a 5-by-10 array along a bookshelf. He claims that the volume of books that the shelf can hold is equal to 50 cubic units. Is his claim correct? If not, explain how he could find the volume.

4. Gill creates a model prism using 22 unit cubes. What is the volume of the prism?

   A 11 units

   B 22 units

   C 22 cubic units

   D 66 cubic units

5. A box has a volume of 64 cubic units. How many cubes with a volume of 1 cubic unit can fit in the box?

   A 4

   B 8

   C 16

   D 64

6. Walter's father put mulch around some trees in the yard. Walter measured the depth of the mulch. He found that there was 2 inches of mulch around each tree. Does the measurement of 2 inches show exactly how much mulch Walter's father used around each tree? Explain why or why not.

7. A closet measures 5 feet wide and 3 feet deep. Does the measurement of 15 square feet show the volume inside the closet? If not, how could you find the volume inside the closet?

Common Core Standards Practice

5.MD.4 Measure volumes by counting unit cubes, using cubic cm, cubic in, cubic ft, and improvised units.

Count the cubes to determine the volume of each shape. There are no hidden cubes.

1.

 A 10 cubic units
 B 9 cubic units
 C 12 cubic units
 D 5 cubic units

2.

 A 10 cubic units
 B 5 cubic units
 C 8 cubic units
 D 5 cubic units

3.

 A 6 cubic units
 B 8 cubic units
 C 12 cubic units
 D 15 cubic units

4.

 A 6 cubic units
 B 9 cubic units
 C 10 cubic units
 D 15 cubic units

In these shapes, the volume of each cube is 1 cubic centimeters. Find the volume of each shape in cubic centimeters.

5.

_____

6.

_____

7.

_____

8.

_____

9.

_____

10.

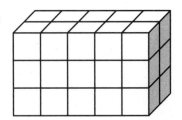

_____

Common Core Standards Practice

5.MD.5a Relate volume to the operations of multiplication and addition and solve real world and mathematical problems involving volume. Find the volume of a right rectangular prism with whole-number side lengths by packing it with unit cubes, and show that the volume is the same as would be found by multiplying the edge lengths, equivalently by multiplying the height by the area of the base. Represent threefold whole-number products as volumes, e.g., to represent the associative property of multiplication.

Find the volumes of the rectangular prisms shown below.

1.

2 cm
2 cm   2 cm

  A 4 cubic cm
  B 6 cubic cm
  C 8 cubic cm
  D 10 cubic cm

2.

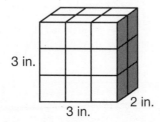

3 in.
3 in.   2 in.

  A 8 cubic in.
  B 9 cubic in.
  C 12 cubic in.
  D 18 cubic in.

3. Tell two ways to find the volume of the box shown below.

5 cm
4 cm   5 cm

One way

Another way

4. Find the volume for each of these rectangular prisms.

3 cm

4 cm

7 cm

a. _____

3 cm

4 cm

9 cm

b. _____

4 in.

4 in.

4 in.

c. _____

2 in.

8 in.

2 in.

d. _____

5. How does knowing the area of one face of a prism help you find the volume of the prism?

Name _____

Common Core Standards Practice

5. MD.5b Relate volume to the operations of multiplication and addition and solve real world and mathematical problems involving volume. Apply the formulas $V = l \times w \times h$ and $V = b \times h$ for rectangular prisms to find volumes of right rectangular prisms with whole-number edge lengths in the context of solving real world and mathematical problems.

1. A milk carton is in the shape of a rectangular prism that is 6 inches long, 4 inches wide, and 4 inches tall. What is its volume?

2. A room is in the shape of a rectangular prism that is 13 feet long, 10 feet high, and 11 feet wide. What is its volume?

3. A bank vault is in the shape of a rectangular prism with a floor area of 280 square feet and a height of 19 feet. Calculate its volume.

4. Calculate the volume of the jewelry box shown below.

3 in.

5 in.

9 in.

5. A dumpster is in the shape of a rectangular prism. Its base measures 136 square feet, and its height is 6 feet. What is the volume of the dumpster?

6. The antique bottle shown below consists of a rectangular prism and a cylinder-shaped spout. Find the volume of the prism section of the bottle.

6 in.

4 in.   3 in.

7. Kyle will fill the candle mold shown below with liquid wax. Find the amount of liquid wax that the mold can hold.

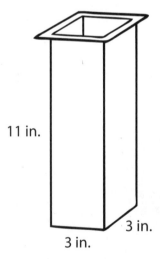

11 in.

3 in.   3 in.

8. Victor keeps a rabbit in a cage that has the shape of a rectangular prism. The ends of the cage measures 4 square feet and the cage is 3 feet long. What is the volume of the cage?

Name _____

Common Core Standards Practice

5. MD.5c Relate volume to the operations of multiplication and addition and solve real world and mathematical problems involving volume. Recognize volume as additive. Find volumes of solid figures composed of two non-overlapping right rectangular prisms by adding the volumes of the non-overlapping parts, applying this technique to solve real world problems.

Find the volume of each individual prism. Then add the volumes to find the volume of the combined prisms.

1.

 +

_____ cubic inches + _____ cubic inches = _____ cubic inches

2.

  +   =

_____ cubic meters + _____ cubic meters = _____ cubic meters

Find the volume of these shapes. Each was made by joining two rectangular prisms together.

3.

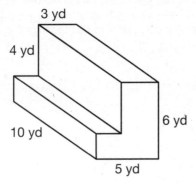

3 yd
4 yd
10 yd
6 yd
5 yd

4.

6 in.
9 in.
5 in.
3 in.
2 in.

5.

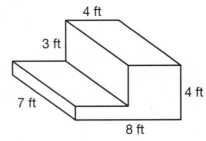

4 ft
3 ft
7 ft
4 ft
8 ft

6.

1 in.
5 in.
4 in.
3 in.
4 in.

7. A moving truck has a floor space that is 14 feet long, 8 feet wide, and 9 feet tall. The truck also has an additional space at the front of the truck that is 3 feet long, 4 feet tall, and the same width as the rest of the truck. How much space is there inside the moving truck?

CC 58

Name _____

Common Core Standards Practice

5.G.1 Use a pair of perpendicular number lines, called axes, to define a coordinate system, with the intersection of the lines (the origin) arranged to coincide with the 0 on each line and a given point in the plane located by using an ordered pair of numbers, called its coordinates. Understand that the first number indicates how far to travel from the origin in the direction of one axis, and the second number indicates how far to travel in the direction of the second axis, with the convention that the names of the two axes and the coordinates correspond (e.g., *x*-axis and *x*-coordinate, *y*-axis and *y*-coordinate).

Use the coordinate plane below for Exercises 1–3.

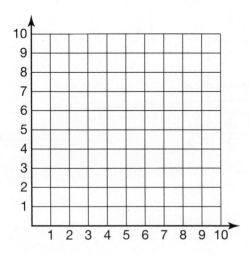

1. Label these parts of the coordinate plane.

   a. *x*-axis

   b. *y*-axis

   c. *O*

2. Draw and label a line to show where the *x*-coordinate is always equal to 6.

3. Draw and label a line to show where the *y*-coordinate is always equal to 3.

Use the coordinate plane below to find the point that matches each description. Name each point with a letter and its coordinates.

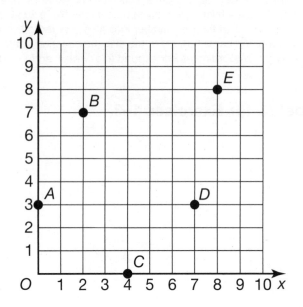

4. the point on the *x*-axis _____

5. the point on the *y*-axis _____

6. the point that has an *x*-coordinate of 7 _____

7. the point that has a *y*-coordinate of 7 _____

8. the point that has *x*- and *y*-coordinates that equal each other _____

CC 60

Name _____

Common Core Standards Practice

5.G.2 Represent real world and mathematical problems by graphing points in the first quadrant of the coordinate plane, and interpret coordinate values of points in the context of the situation.

1. Write the coordinates for the points shown in the coordinate plane.

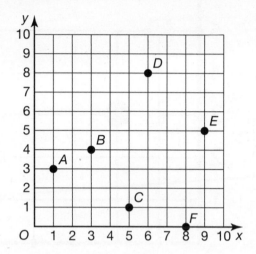

A(_____, _____)   D(_____, _____)

B(_____, _____)   E(_____, _____)

C(_____, _____)   F(_____, _____)

2. Graph and label these points in the coordinate plane.

A(3, 4)   D(8, 9)

B(5, 5)   E(2, 8)

C(7, 2)   F(0, 5)

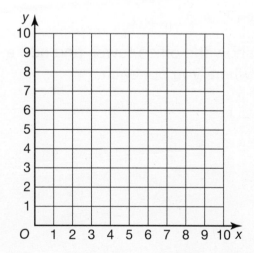

3. Downtown has streets and avenues that fit the coordinate plane, as shown in the map below.

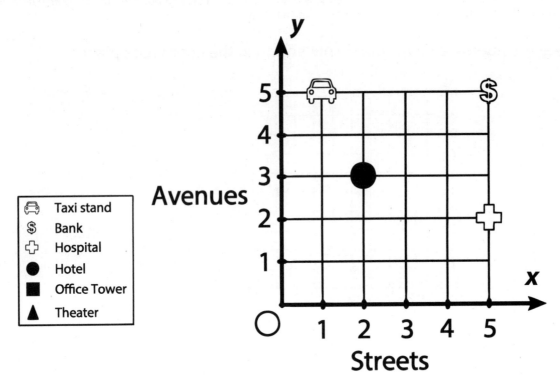

The taxi stand is at the corner of 1ˢᵗ Street and 5ᵗʰ Avenue.

Name the locations of the other places.

a. Hotel:

b. Bank:

c. Hospital:

4. Add a square to the map to show the office tower, and add a triangle to show the theater. Identify where you put each.

a. Office tower: (_____, _____)

b. Theater: (_____, _____)

Name _____

Common Core Standards Practice

5.G.3 Understand that attributes belonging to a category of two-dimensional figures also belong to all subcategories of that category.

1. What properties do isosceles and equilateral triangles share?

2. What properties do rhombuses and parallelograms share?

3. Here are a rectangle, a square, and a rhombus.

    a. What are the common properties of the rectangle and the square?

    b. What are the common properties of the square and the rhombus?

    c. Of the three figures, which could also be classified as either of the other two figures? Explain.

4. Name a common property of trapezoids and quadrilaterals.

5. Put check marks in the table to show each figure that has the given property.

Property	Quadrilateral	Parallelogram	Trapezoid	Rectangle	Rhombus	Square
This figure has four sides.						
This figure always has two pairs of parallel sides.						
This figure has only one pair of parallel sides.						
This figure always has four right angles.						
This figure always has four sides of equal length.						

Name _____

Common Core Standards Practice

5.G.4 Classify two-dimensional figures in a hierarchy based on properties.

1. A triangle has one right angle. Two of its sides are equal in length. Which terms describe the triangle? Circle all that apply.

   right   isosceles   scalene   equilateral

Use the chart below to help you classify quadrilaterals.

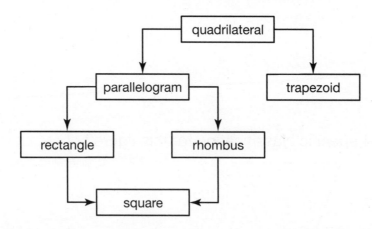

2. A figure has four sides and four right angles. The lengths of its sides are not all equal to each other. Which names could describe the figure? Circle all that apply.

   quadrilateral   trapezoid   parallelogram   rhombus   rectangle   square

3. Name the figure in as many ways as possible.

   A quadrilateral

   B quadrilateral, parallelogram

   C quadrilateral, trapezoid

   D quadrilateral, parallelogram, rhombus

4. Name this figure.

5. Name this figure in as many ways as possible.

6. Select the most specific classification for a figure that has four sides of equal length, but not four angles of equal measure.

  A quadrilateral

  B parallelogram

  C rhombus

  D trapezoid

7. What is the most specific classification for this figure?

  A quadrilateral   **C** trapezoid

  B parallelogram   **D** rhombus

8. Why are all rectangles examples of parallelograms, but all parallelograms are not rectangles?

9. Circle the statements that are true.

All squares are rectangles.

All rhombuses are squares.

All quadrilaterals are trapezoids.

All rhombuses are parallelograms.

All parellograms are quadrilaterals.

Practice End-of-Year Assessment

1. Tell two ways you can use to find the volume of a rectangular prism.

One Way	**Another Way**

2. A triangle has three sides of equal length. Circle the categories in which the triangle can be classified.

equilateral   isosceles   right   scalene

3. A rectangular rug is $5\frac{3}{4}$ feet wide and $7\frac{1}{2}$ feet long. What is the area of the rug?

4. To make a lace border for a hat, Rebecca uses $\frac{5}{12}$ yard of red lace and $\frac{1}{6}$ yard of green lace.

    a. Model the problem with this circle.

    b. How much lace does Rebecca use to make her hat?

5. Cassie's cat weighs $3\frac{1}{2}$ pounds. Her dog weighs 4 times as much as her cat. How much does her dog weigh?

6. Which describes the relationship between 15,700 and 157,000?

    A 15,700 is $\frac{1}{10}$ of 157,000.

    B 157,000 is $\frac{1}{10}$ of 15,700.

    C 15,700 is $\frac{1}{100}$ of 157,000.

    D 157,000 is $\frac{1}{100}$ of 15,700.

7. Find the quotient.

    $1,633 \div 23$.

8. The line plot shows the birth weights, in pounds, of a litter of 8 puppies.

   a. What is the difference in weight between the heaviest and lightest puppy?

   b. Which birth weight was most common among the puppies?

9. How is the value of 3 in the number 43,442 different from the value of 3 in the number 44,432?

10. Which model matches the division expression?

    $3 \div 4$

    A

    B

    C

    D

11. Label the *x*-axis, *y*-axis, and origin on the coordinate grid shown below. Use the letter "O" for the origin.

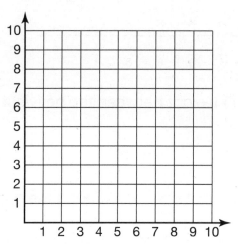

12. Match these numbers with their expanded forms.

7.5 $7 \times 1 + 0 \times \frac{1}{10} + 5 \times \frac{1}{100}$

7.05 $1 \times 1000 + 6 \times 100 + 8 \times 1$

16.09 $1 \times 10 + 6 \times 1 + 9 \times \frac{1}{100}$

1,608 $7 \times 1 + 5 \times \frac{1}{10}$

13. Divide.

0.84 ÷ 0.07

14. Which of these numbers, when rounded to the nearest tenth, is 0.8? Circle all that round to 0.8.

0.76   0.84   0.72   0.079   0.79

15. Look at the following pairs of values.

x	y
1	5
2	8
3	11
4	14
5	17

a. What is the rule for each column?

b. Write two more pairs of values that could be added to this table.

c. Graph these pairs of values on the coordinate grid. What do you notice about the graph of these values?

16. Dao has a cookie recipe that calls for $3\frac{1}{4}$ cups of flour. He plans to make $1\frac{1}{2}$ batches of cookies. Explain whether Dao will need more flour, less flour, or the same amount of flour as his recipe calls for.

17. Write the expressions in the appropriate place. You should NOT find the products of the expressions.

Less than 3	Equal to 3	Greater than 3

$\frac{1}{3} \times 3$ $\frac{6}{6} \times 3$ $\frac{7}{6} \times 3$ $3 \times \frac{7}{7}$

$3 \times \frac{3}{2}$ $3 \times \frac{2}{5}$ $3 \times \frac{9}{7}$ $\frac{1}{4} \times 6$

18. Tell whether the equation is true. Justify your answer.

$36 - (12 + 8) \div 4 \overset{?}{=} 36 - 12 + 8 \div 4$

19. Complete the table.

32.8 ÷ 1	32.8
32.8 ÷ 10	
32.8 ÷ 100	
32.8 ÷ 1,000	

Describe the pattern in the table.

20. The length of a rectangular window is $5\frac{3}{4}$ feet and its width is $3\frac{1}{2}$ feet. What is the area of the window?

21. Plot points M and L on the coordinate grid.

   a. Point M: (7, 3)

   b. Point L: (3, 1)

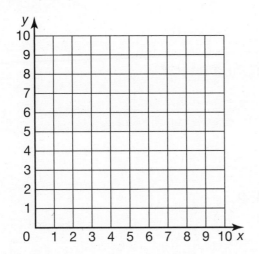

22. Paula covers her bathroom with pink and white tiles. Each tile is the same size. She uses $2\frac{1}{2}$ times more pink tiles than white tiles, and the white tiles cover $4\frac{1}{2}$ square feet. How much area do the pink tiles cover?

23. A concert hall has 2,312 seats. For one concert, each seat is sold for $89. What is the total amount of money in ticket sales if the concert is sold out?

24. A recipe calls for $\frac{2}{3}$ cup of brown sugar to make one batch of muffins. Amanda plans to make $5\frac{1}{2}$ batches of muffins.

a. Draw a model to match the problem situation.

b. How much brown sugar will Amanda need?

25. Find the product of 1,275 and 23,452.

26. Which of these are equal to the sum of $\frac{4}{12}$ and $\frac{6}{8}$? Circle all that are equal to the sum.

$\frac{10}{20}$　　　　$\frac{26}{24}$　　　　$\frac{10}{12}$　　　　$\frac{13}{12}$　　　　$1\frac{1}{12}$　　　　$1\frac{2}{12}$

27. Mary studied math for $1\frac{1}{2}$ hours and science for $\frac{3}{5}$ hour. How many hours did she spend studying?

28. Which expression matches this statement?
four times the difference of 12 and 2

    A $4 + 12 - 2$

    B $12 - 2 \times 4$

    C $4 \times (12 - 2)$

    D $4 \times 12 - 2$

29. A dolphin ate 2,604 pounds of fish during the 31 days of March.

    a. What is the average amount of fish the dolphin ate per day?

    b. Draw a model to justify your answer.

30. Pineapples cost $2.19 each. Watermelons cost $2.91 each.

    a. Which costs more: a pineapple or a watermelon?

    b. Write a number sentence to compare the two prices.

31. A group of 6 friends wants to share 8 pears evenly. All of the pears are the same size.

   a. How many pears should each friend receive?

   b. Explain how the friends should cut the pears and divide them.

32. Drake has a piece of blue ribbon that is $\frac{1}{8}$ yard long, and a silver ribbon that is $\frac{3}{4}$ yard long. How much longer is the silver ribbon?

33. Amy has 6 cups of applesauce. She divides the applesauce into $\frac{1}{2}$-cup servings.

   a. Draw a model to match the problem.

   b. How many servings of applesauce does she have?

34. A sporting goods factory produces 13,234 tennis balls per month. How many tennis balls does it produce during 12 months?

35. Emilio builds a flower planter in the shape of a rectangular prism. It is 4 feet long, 2 feet high, and 2 feet wide. What is the volume of the planter?

36. Four friends share $\frac{1}{4}$ of a cake. What fraction of the whole cake does each friend get?

37. Which term could describe each of these three figures?

   A square
   B rhombus
   C rectangle
   D parallelogram

38. Which of these are equal to the difference of $\frac{4}{6}$ and $\frac{2}{9}$? Circle all that are equal to the difference.

$\frac{1}{9}$ $\frac{4}{9}$ $\frac{2}{3}$ $\frac{8}{18}$ $\frac{3}{6}$ $\frac{8}{9}$

39. Find the volume of the rectangular prism shown below.

8 cm

6 cm

11 cm

40. Multiply.

9.3 × 4.27

41. Draw a model to find the product of $\frac{3}{8}$ × 4. Then find the product.

42. What is 17.264 rounded to the nearest hundredth?

    A 17.26

    B 17.27

    C 17.3

    D 17.24

43. Bargain Toys packs 1,440 toys onto 40 shelves. Each shelf holds the same number of toys. How many toys are on each shelf?

44. Circle all of the expressions that equal 1,483,000.

    1.483×10^6 14.83×10^6 148.3×10^4

    148.3×10^3 1.483×10^7 14.83×10^5

45. Mr. Lee's fence is 10 yards long. How many feet long is the fence?

Name _____

Performance Task 1

Storage Needs

Part A

Erica makes and sells homemade salad dressings. She packages the dressings in small jars, which she then places in boxes that hold 6 jars. The dimensions of the shipping boxes are 1 foot by 1 foot by 1 foot.

Erica has two different storage spaces for the boxes. One of the spaces is 4 feet long by 3 wide feet by 6 feet high. The other space measures 5 feet long by 3 feet wide by 5 feet high.

1. Into which storage area can Erica fit more boxes of dressing? How many more boxes can she fit into the larger area? Explain your answer with models.

Part B

Erica would like to increase the production of her salad dressings. To do so, she will need more storage space for boxes of jars. Erica has two options for additional storage space. Storage space C is 4 feet long by 6 feet wide by 6 feet high and storage space D is 8 feet long by 4 feet wide by 5 feet high. Including her original storage area, Erica would like to have a total of at least 280 cubic feet, but no more than 300 cubic feet, of storage space.

2. Which of the two additional storage space options should Erica choose? Explain your reasoning for the option you selected.

Name _____

Performance Task 2

Town Beautification

Part A

The Town Council in Center City will start a tree-planting program to beautify parts of the town. The plan calls for planting 2,000 trees. Below are three types of trees that have been recommended and are available for planting:

Type of Tree	Cost per Tree (including tax)
Cherry	$40.50
Dogwood	$65.00
Myrtle	$50.50

The Town Council voted to budget $100,000 to buy the 2,000 trees. Both the Parks Department, which will purchase and plant the trees, and the Town Council, agree that there should be a mix of all three types of trees.

The towns people were also surveyed about which types of trees to plant. The result of the survey show that cherry trees are a town favorite, so the Town Council has recommended that at least half of the trees planted by cherry trees.

1. You have been asked by the Parks Department to determine how many of each type of tree the Parks Department should purchase and the total cost. In your proposal, you should come as close as you can to spending all of the money budgeted for the purchase of the trees. You need to answer these questions in your proposal:

   a. What is the total number of each type of tree to be planted?

   b. What is the total amount needed to purchase each type of tree?

   c. What is the total amount needed to purchase all types of trees?

Part B

The Parks Department will be responsible for planting all of the trees for the tree-planting program. According to the tree nursery, each newly planted tree will need a layer of organic mulch. The nursery estimates that each cherry tree planted will require 20 pounds of mulch, each dogwood tree 25 pounds of mulch, and each myrtle tree 20 pounds of mulch. The nursery sells mulch for $34.95 a ton. It does not sell fractions of a ton.

2. How much money will the Parks Department need in order to purchase mulch for all of the trees in your proposal?

Practice End-of-Year Assessment
Test 2

1. Small cubes were joined together to form a larger cube, as shown below.

   a. Explain how to find the volume of the large cube.

   b. What is the volume of the large cube?

2. Circle the categories in which this figure can be classified.

   4 cm

   4 cm

   quadrilateral   square   rhombus   parallelogram   rectangle

3. A rectangular painting is $1\frac{2}{3}$ feet long and $1\frac{1}{2}$ feet high. What is the area
   of the painting?

4. Sarah and Ann are painting a wall in Ann's bedroom. On the first day, Sarah paints $\frac{1}{4}$ of the wall, and Ann paints $\frac{1}{3}$ of the wall.

   a. Model the problem with this square.

   b. How much of the wall is left to paint?

5. Kento's recipe for a batch of muffins calls for $2\frac{1}{2}$ cups of flour. How much flour would Kento need to make $3\frac{1}{2}$ batches of muffins?

6. Which describes the relationship between 70,070 and 7,007?

   A 70,070 is 10 times 7,007.

   B 70,070 is 100 times 7,007.

   C 70,070 is $\frac{1}{10}$ of 7,007.

   D 70,070 is $\frac{1}{100}$ of 7,007.

7. Find the quotient.

   $9,888 \div 16$

8. Chan walks dogs every afternoon. The table shows the amount of time he walked dogs each day during the past week.

Time Spent Walking Dogs (hours)						
$\frac{1}{2}$	$\frac{3}{4}$	$\frac{1}{4}$	$\frac{1}{2}$	$\frac{3}{4}$	$\frac{1}{2}$	$\frac{1}{4}$

a. Make a line plot of the data.

b. What was the most common time spent walking dogs?

c. What was the greatest difference in time spent walking dogs?

9. A five-digit number is made from the digits 6, 6, 3, 3, and 3. Write two numbers in which the places of the two 6's are separated by a factor of 1,000?

10. Which model matches the division expression?

$4 \div 6$

A

B

C

D

11. On the coordinate grid, what is the name of the point where the *x*-axis meets the *y*-axis?

12. Match these numbers with their expanded forms.

70.6 $1 \times 1000 + 4 \times 100 + 3 \times 1$

7.06 $7 \times 100 + 6 \times \frac{1}{10}$

14.3 $7 \times 1 + 6 \times \frac{1}{100}$

1403 $1 \times 10 + 4 \times 1 + 3 \times \frac{1}{10}$

13. Find the quotient.

$3.84 \div 0.96$

14. Which of these numbers, when rounded to the nearest hundredth, is 0.56? Circle all that round to 0.56.

0.566   0.556   0.563   0.554   0.555   0.565

15. Look at the following pairs of values.

x	y
1	2
2	4
3	6
4	8
5	10

   a. What is the rule for each column?

   b. Write two more pairs of values that could be added to this table.

   c. Graph these pairs of values on the coordinate grid. What do you notice about the graph of these values?

16. Fred cuts a 12-inch piece of rope. Then he cuts a second piece of rope that is $\frac{3}{2}$ longer than the first piece. Is the second piece shorter or longer than the first piece? Explain how you know.

17. Write the expressions in the appropriate place. You should NOT find the products of the expressions.

Less than 5	Equal to 5	Greater than 5

$5 \times \dfrac{2}{3}$ 　　　$\dfrac{3}{4} \times 5$ 　　　$5 \times \dfrac{3}{3}$ 　　　$\dfrac{4}{4} \times 5$

$5 \times \dfrac{5}{3}$ 　　　$\dfrac{3}{2} \times 5$ 　　　$5 \times \dfrac{8}{5}$ 　　　$\dfrac{2}{5} \times 5$

18. Tell whether the equation is true. Justify your answer.

$24 \times 3 + (15 - 7) \div 2 \overset{?}{=} 8 \times 9 + 12 \div 2$

19. Complete the table.

$72.4 \div 1$	
$72.4 \div 10^1$	
$72.4 \div 10^2$	
$72.4 \div 10^3$	

Describe the pattern in the table.

20. The dimensions of a rectangular photo frame are $4\frac{1}{3}$ in. by $3\frac{1}{3}$ in. What is the area of the photo frame?

21. Write the coordinates of each animal picture on the coordinate grid.

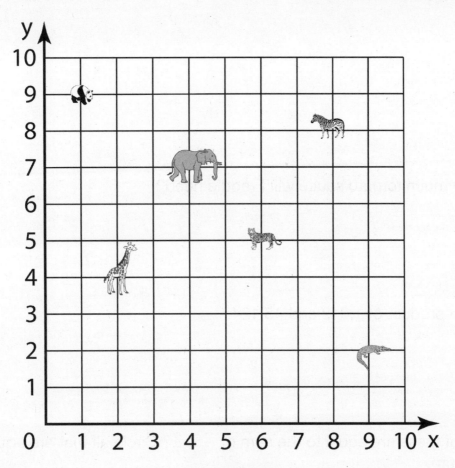

a. Zebra

b. Alligator

c. Tiger

d. Elephant

e. Panda

f. Giraffe

22. Lee can sew $3\frac{3}{4}$ sock monkeys in one hour. How many sock monkeys can he sew in $6\frac{1}{2}$ hours of work?

23. Find the product of 2,212 and 95.

24. A recipe calls for $\frac{3}{4}$ cup of tomato sauce to make one batch of spaghetti sauce. Freddie plans to make $3\frac{1}{2}$ batches of spaghetti sauce.

  a. Draw a model to match the problem situation.

  b. How much tomato sauce will Freddie need?

25. Find the product of 1,012 and 45,124.

26. Which of these are equal to the sum of $\frac{7}{12} + \frac{7}{8}$? Circle all that are equal to the sum.

$\frac{14}{20}$	$\frac{35}{24}$	$\frac{14}{12}$
$\frac{17}{12}$	$1\frac{11}{24}$	$1\frac{5}{12}$

27. To make trail mix, Andre adds $\frac{3}{5}$ cup of peanuts and $\frac{2}{3}$ cut of walnuts. How many cups of nuts are in the trail mix?

28. Which expression matches this statement?

45 is divided by the sum of 9 and 6.

A $45 \div 9 + 6$

B $(45 \div 9) + 6$

C $45 \div (9 + 6)$

D $45 + 9 \div 6$

29. The Tran family drove 1,246 miles during a vacation that lasted 14 days.

a. How many miles on average did they drive each day?

b. Draw a model to justify your answer.

30. In a track and field event, the times of the top three finishers were 9.85 seconds, 9.9 seconds, and 9.82 seconds.

a. Order the times from least to greatest.

b. Write a number sentence to compare the three times.

CC 93

31. A group of 5 friends bakes 8 pies. All of the pies are the same size. The 5 friends will share the pies equally.

    a. How much pie should each friend receive?

    b. Explain how the friends could share the pies.

32. During a movie, Russell ate $\frac{4}{5}$ of a bucket of popcorn and Jack ate $\frac{3}{4}$ of a bucket of popcorn. How much more popcorn did Russell eat?

33. James has 4 apples. He slices each apple into quarters.

    a. Draw a model to match the problem.

    b. How many $\frac{1}{4}$-apple slices does he have?

34. Pop's Pizza makes an average of 11,234 pizzas per month. How many pizzas do they make in a year?

35. Hanh is looking at a fish aquarium. It is in the shape of a rectangular prism that is 2 feet wide, 5 feet long, and 2 feet tall. What is the volume of the fish tank?

36. Anna's mother baked a plum cake and gave $\frac{1}{2}$ of it to Anna. Anna divided the piece equally among 6 friends. What fraction of the whole cake did each friend get?

37. Which term best describes these three figures?

    A irregular polygons

    B regular polygons

    C quadrilaterals

    D hexagons

38. Which of these are equal to the difference of $\frac{1}{3}$ and $\frac{1}{7}$? Circle all that are equal to the difference.

$\frac{2}{10}$ $\frac{10}{21}$ $\frac{4}{21}$ $\frac{2}{3}$ $\frac{0}{4}$ $\frac{4}{10}$

39. Find the volume of the rectangular prism shown below.

8 cm

8 cm

14 cm

40. Multiply.

2.62 × 3.5

41. Draw a model to find the product of $3 \times \frac{3}{4}$. Then find the product.

42. What is 0.367 rounded to the nearest hundredth?

    A 0.3

    B 0.36

    C 0.37

    D 0.4

43. A local charity received 1,800 blankets. They distribute them equally to 36 local shelters. How many blankets will each shelter receive?

44. Which of these expressions are equivalent to 54,200,000? Circle all of the expressions.

    5.42×10^7 5.42×10^6 54.2×10^6

    542×10^5 54.2×10^7 5.42×10^8

45. The height of a room is 9 feet. What is the height in inches?

Name _____

Performance Task 3

Arts and Crafts

Part A

Amanda and her mother decorate picture frames to sell at craft shows. They put decorative ribbon around the frames, with a one-inch overlap. On some frames they add a decorative bow, which requires an additional $3\frac{1}{2}$ inches of ribbon.

Amanda has 10 feet of striped ribbon. She wants to be able to decorate five frames, two small frames that are 4 in. by 6 in., one medium-sized frame that is 5 in. by 7 in.; and two large frames that are 8 in. by 10 in.

1. Does Amanda have enough ribbon to decorate the five frames? Justify your answer by showing how much ribbon she needs for each frame and the total amount of ribbon she would use. Use models or equations to support your answer.

2. If Amanda has enough ribbon, what could she do with the remaining ribbon? If she does not have enough ribbon, how should she adjust her plans to maximize ribbon use?

CC 98

Part B

Amanda and her mother have these frames to sell at the craft fair. They plan to sell the 4 in. × 6 in. frames for $5, the 5 in. × 7 in. frames for $8, and the 8 in. × 10 in. frames for $10. They charge an extra dollar for frames with a bow.

Frame Size	Number
4 in. × 6 in. with bow	5
4 in. × 6 in. without bow	5
5 in. × 7 in. with bow	4
5 in. × 7 in. without bow	6
8 in. × 10 in. with bow	5
8 in. × 10 in. without bow	3

3. They would like to make $150 from selling frames at the craft fair. Will they be able to achieve their goal? If yes, explain how you know. Then describe one way that they can make $150. If not, explain why it is not possible.

4. If Amanda and her mother decide to add a bow to all of the frames before selling them, how should they price the frames so that they can make at least $300 if they sell all of their frames?

Name _____

Performance Task 4
Yogurt Containers
Part A

Amy's family owns a frozen yogurt business. They have small yogurt cups that hold $\frac{1}{2}$ cup of frozen yogurt and medium cups that hold $\frac{3}{4}$ cup of frozen yogurt. The table below shows the number of cups sold in one day.

Cup Size	Number of Cups Sold
small	28
medium	16

1. Amy's family made 5 gallons of frozen yogurt. How many days will it take before they run out of frozen yogurt? (Assume that the data in the table is representative of daily sales.)

2. They make frozen yogurt in batches that are 5 gallons each. How many batches of frozen yogurt will they need to make to have enough for one week?

Part B

The table from Part A showed the sales on a weekday when school was in session. Amy's family sells $1\frac{1}{2}$ times as much frozen yogurt on a weekday when school is not in session. They sell $2\frac{1}{4}$ times as much frozen yogurt on weekend days.

3. How much yogurt do you think Amy's family will need to make for one week when school is in session?

4. How much frozen yogurt do you think Amy's family should make each week when school is not in session?

5. What other factors might Amy's family want to consider when deciding how much frozen yogurt to make each week?

Answers and Rubrics

Name _____

Common Core Standards Practice

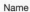

5.OA.1 Use parentheses, brackets, or braces in numerical expressions, and evaluate expressions with these symbols.

1. Which expression is equal to 2?

   A $24 \div (2 + 2) \times 5$
   B $(24 \div 2) + (2 \times 5)$
   C $(24 \div 2 + 2) \times 5$
   Ⓓ $24 \div (2 + 2 \times 5)$

2. Tell whether the equation is true. Justify your answer.

   $2 + 1 \times 5 - 3 \stackrel{?}{=} (2 + 1) \times (5 - 3)$

   No, the equation is not true. The value of the left side of the equation is 4 and the value of the right side of the equation is 6.

3. Evaluate the expression below.

   $(9 + 2) \times 6 - 5$

   61

4. Evaluate the expression.

   $5 \div (4 - 3) \cdot 3$

   15

5. Evaluate the expression.

   $20 \div (5 \times 2) + 3$

   Ⓐ 5
   B 9
   C 11
   D 12

6. Which expression is equal to 7?

   Ⓐ $(5 + 2) \times [6 - (3 + 2)]$
   B $5 + 2 \times 6 - (3 + 2)$
   C $(5 + 2) \times 6 - (3 + 2)$
   D $(5 + 2) \times [6 - (3 \times 2)]$

CC 1 · Copyright © Pearson Education, Inc., or its affiliates. All Rights Reserved. 5

page CC 1

---

7. Kevin evaluated the expression below.

   $75 - [6(8 - 6) + 3]$

   • Step 1: $75 - [6 \cdot 2 + 3]$
   • Step 2: $75 - [6 \cdot 5]$
   • Step 3: $75 - 30$
   • Step 4: 45

   The teacher finds an error in Kevin's work.

   a. Which step contains the error?

   Step 2.

   b. Explain the error.

   Kevin first added 2 + 3 instead of first multiplying 6 by 2. Multiplication is carried out before addition.

8. Two students simplified the following expression.

Alexandra	Joe
$30 \div 2 - 4 \times 3 + 2$	$30 \div 2 - 4 \times 3 + 2$
$= 15 - 4 \times 3 + 2$	$= 15 - 4 \times 3 + 2$
$= 15 - 12 + 2$	$= 15 - 12 + 2$
$= 3 + 2$	$= 15 - 14$
$= 5$	$= 1$

   a. Which student simplified the expression correctly?

   Alexandra is correct.

   b. What mistake was made?

   Joe added 12 + 2 when he should have first subtracted 15 and 12.

CC 2 · Copyright © Pearson Education, Inc., or its affiliates. All Rights Reserved. 5

page CC 2

Name _____

Common Core Standards Practice

5.OA.2 Write simple expressions that record calculations with numbers, and interpret numerical expressions without evaluating them.

1. Which expression matches this statement?

   Divide 24 by 6 less than 8.

   Ⓐ $24 \div (8 - 6)$
   B $24 \div 8 - 6$
   C $(24 \div 6) - 8$
   D $[(24 \div 8) - 6]$

2. Each row in a box of chocolates contains 4 caramels and 8 creams. Which expression represents the number of chocolates in a box with 3 rows of chocolates?

   A $3 + (4 \times 8)$
   Ⓑ $3 \times (4 + 8)$
   C $(3 \times 4) + (2 \times 8)$
   D $(4 \times 8) \times 3$

3. The price of an adult ticket to the museum is $6.00. The price of a student ticket is $4.00. Write an expression to represent the cost of 4 adult tickets and 8 student tickets.

   $(4 \times 6) + (8 \times 4)$

4. Write an expression to match the statement below.

   Add 5 to 48 divided by 12.

   $48 \div 12 + 5$ or $5 + 48 \div 12$

5. Latisha and Raquel ordered two beverages for $1.50 each, two dinners for $12.99 each, and one dessert to share for $3.50. Which expression represents the cost of the meal for each person?

   A $1.50 + 2 \times 12.99 + 3.50 \div 2$
   Ⓑ $(2 \times 1.50 + 2 \times 12.99 + 3.50) \div 2$
   C $2 \times (1.50 + 12.99 + 3.50)$
   D $(2 \times 1.50 + 12.99) + 3.50 \div 2$

6. Which expression matches the statement below?

   Find the product of 50 minus 5 and 4 divided by 2.

   Ⓐ $(50 - 5) \times (4 \div 2)$
   B $50 - 5 \times 4 \div 2$
   C $50 \div 5 \times 4 \div 2$
   D $50 - 5 + 4 \div 2$

7. Write an expression to match the statement below.

   Divide the product of 4 and 5 by the sum of 2 and 8.

   $(4 \times 5) \div (2 + 8)$

8. The table below shows the cost of several items sold at The Clothes Shack.

The Clothes Shack	
Item	**Price per article ($)**
Jeans	30
T-Shirt	15
Sweatshirt	20
Caps	10

   Jason went to the Clothes Shack with $150. Write an expression to represent the amount of money Jason has remaining after buying 2 pairs of jeans, 3 T-shirts, and 2 sweatshirts.

   $150 - [(2 \times 30) + (3 \times 15) + (2 \times 20)]$

CC 3 · Copyright © Pearson Education, Inc., or its affiliates. All Rights Reserved. 5

page CC 3

CC 4 · Copyright © Pearson Education, Inc., or its affiliates. All Rights Reserved. 5

page CC 4

page CC 5

Common Core Standards Practice

5.OA.3 Generate two numerical patterns using two given rules. Identify apparent relationships between corresponding terms. Form ordered pairs consisting of corresponding terms from the two patterns, and graph the ordered pairs on a coordinate plane.

1. a. Generate two numerical sequences using the rules shown below.

Add 5: 0, __5__, __10__, __15__, __20__

Add 20: 0, __20__, __40__, __60__, __80__

b. What relationship can you find between the second term in first sequence and the second term in the second sequence?

The second term in the second sequence is 4 times the second term in the first sequence.

c. Does this relationship hold for all corresponding terms in the two sequences? Tell how you know.

Yes, all corresponding terms in the second sequence are 4 times the term in the first sequence.

2. Complete the following table.

Add 8.	8	16	24	32	40
Subtract 2.	2	4	6	8	10

page CC 6

3. Ama is emptying a large container of water. The container has 100 gallons of water. Ama opens the valve so that 5 gallons of water flow out each minute.

a. Complete a table to show how much water flows out of the container over time.

Minutes	0	1	2	3	4	5	6
Number of gallons	100	95	90	85	80	75	70

b. Write ordered pairs for each set of values in the table.

(0, 100), (1, 95), (2, 90), (3, 85), (4, 80), (5, 75), (6, 70)

c. Plot the ordered pairs on the coordinate grid.

4. a. Write four ordered pairs by applying the rules "subtract 1 from the x-coordinate" and "add 2 to the y-coordinate." Begin at (5,0).

Ordered Pairs: (5, 0), (__4__ , __2__), (__3__ , __4__), (__2__ , __6__), (__1__ , __8__)

b. Graph the ordered pairs on the grid.

page CC 7

Common Core Standards Practice

5.NBT.1 Recognize that in a multi-digit number, a digit in one place represents 10 times as much as it represents in the place to its right and $\frac{1}{10}$ of what it represents in the place to its left.

1. How much greater is 500 than 5?

A 5 times greater
B 10 times greater
Ⓒ 100 times greater
D 1000 times greater

2. Which describes the relationship between 20,000 and 200,000?

A 20,000 is 10 times as much as 200,000.

B 200,000 is $\frac{1}{10}$ of 20,000.

C 20,000 is $\frac{1}{100}$ of 200,000.

Ⓓ 20,000 is $\frac{1}{10}$ of 200,000.

3. How is the value of 2 in the number 542 different from the value of 2 in the number 324?

The 2 in 542 represents 2 ones or 2, while the 2 in 324 represents 2 tens or 20.

4. How is the value of 4 in 864 related to the value of 4 in 846?

The value of the 4 in the number 864 is $\frac{1}{10}$ of its value in the number 846.

page CC 8

5. How much greater is 300 than 3?

A 10 times
Ⓑ 100 times
C 1,000 times
D 10,000 times

6. What is the relationship between 5,000 and 500,000?

A 5,000 is $\frac{1}{10}$ the value of 500,000.

Ⓑ 5,000 is $\frac{1}{100}$ the value of 500,000.

C 5,000 is 100 times the value of 500,000.

D 5,000 is 10 times the value of 500,000.

7. What is the difference in place value between the 2 in 324 and the 2 in 0.324?

The value of 2 in 324 is 2 tens or 20. The value of 2 in 0.324 is 2 hundredths or 0.02.

8. The total number of people who visited the Ocean Adventure Park last year was 7,040,836. What is the value of the digit 4 in this number?

The value of the digit 4 is 4 ten thousands or 40,000.

9. How many tenths are in 13.58?

5 tenths.

10. How many hundredths are in 401.308?

0 hundredths.

page CC 9

Name _____

Common Core Standards Practice

5.NBT.2 Explain patterns in the number of zeros of the product when multiplying a number by powers of 10, and explain patterns in the placement of the decimal point when a decimal is multiplied or divided by a power of 10. Use whole-number exponents to denote powers of 10.

1. Circle all of the expressions that equal 372,000.

   (372 × 10³)   3.72 × 10⁶   372 × 10⁴

   (37.2 × 10⁴)   37.2 × 10³   (3.72 × 10⁵)

2. Complete the table.

Expression	Product
5 × 10¹	50
5 × 10²	**500**
5 × 10³	**5,000**
5 × 10⁴	**50,000**

What pattern do you observe in the table?

As the exponent in the power of 10 increases by 1, the number of zeros in the product also increases by 1.

3. Complete the table.

Expression	Quotient
76 ÷ 10¹	7.6
76 ÷ 10²	**0.76**
76 ÷ 10³	**0.076**
76 ÷ 10⁴	**0.0076**

What pattern do you observe in the table?

As the exponent in the power of 10 increases by 1, the decimal point in the quotient moves 1 digit to the left.

---

page CC 10

4. Draw a model to show the value of this expression.

   5 ÷ 10²

Check students' models. They should show 5 hundredths.

5. Match the numbers on the left with an equivalent expression on the right. Some may have more than one equivalent expression. Some may have no equivalent expressions.

   0.67

   10.67

   4,239

   1067 ÷ 10²

   4.239 ÷ 10³

   67 ÷ 10³

   1.067 × 10¹

   67 ÷ 10²

   4.239 × 10³

6. Circle all of the expressions that are equivalent to 1,795,000.

   (1,795 × 10³)   (17.95 × 10⁵)   1.795 × 10⁷

   179.5 × 10⁵   17.95 × 10⁶   (1,795 × 10³)

---

page CC 11

Name _____

Common Core Standards Practice

5.NBT.3a Read, write, and compare decimals to thousandths. Read and write decimals to thousandths using base-ten numerals, number names, and expanded form.

1. Sharon is writing 4.072 in expanded form. What number makes the equation true?

   4.072 = 4 + 0.0 + ____ + 0.002

   A 7
   B 0.7
   C 0.07
   D 0.007

2. What is the standard form of the number below?

   10 + 1 + 0.9 + 0.02 + 0.003

   A 1192.3
   B 119.23
   C 1.1923
   D 11.923

3. Jeremy has a batting average of 0.235. What is the batting average written in expanded form?

   $2 \times \frac{1}{10} + 3 \times \frac{1}{100} + 5 \times \frac{1}{1000}$

4. Match these numbers with their expanded forms.

   3.6

   3.06

   40.15

   4,015

   $4 \times 10 + 1 \times \frac{1}{10} + 5 \times \frac{1}{100}$

   $3 \times 1 + 6 \times \frac{1}{100}$

   $3 \times 1 + 6 \times \frac{1}{10}$

   $4 \times 1000 + 1 \times 10 + 5 \times 1$

---

page CC 12

5. Which show different forms of 5.39? Circle all that are equal to 5.39.

   A Five and thirty-nine hundredths
   B 539 ÷ 10²
   C 5 + 0.3 + 0.09
   D 5 and 39 tenths
   E 0.539 × 10²
   F 0.539 × 10¹

6. What is the expanded form of five and six hundred fourteen thousandths?

   A 5 + 0.6 + 0.01 + 0.004
   B 5 + 0.06 + 0.01 + 0.004
   C 5 + 0.06 + 0.001 + 0.004
   D 5 + 0.6 + 0.001 + 0.0004

7. Write these expressions in standard form.

   a. $(4 \times 1) + \left(6 \times \frac{1}{10}\right)$
   4.6

   b. $4 \times 10 + 3 \times \frac{1}{10} + 7 \times \frac{1}{100} + 5 \times \frac{1}{1000}$
   40.375

   c. $(9 \times 10) + \left(5 \times \frac{1}{10}\right)$
   90.5

   d. $(9 \times 1) + \left(5 \times \frac{1}{100}\right)$
   9.05

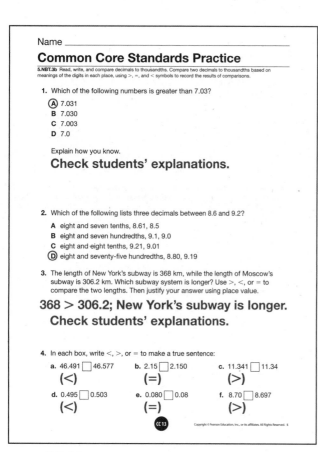

Name _____

Common Core Standards Practice

5.NBT.3b Read, write, and compare decimals to thousandths. Compare two decimals to thousandths based on meanings of the digits in each place, using >, =, and < symbols to record the results of comparisons.

1. Which of the following numbers is greater than 7.03?

   Ⓐ 7.031
   B 7.030
   C 7.003
   D 7.0

   Explain how you know.
   ## Check students' explanations.

2. Which of the following lists three decimals between 8.6 and 9.2?

   A eight and seven tenths, 8.61, 8.5
   B eight and seven hundredths, 9.1, 9.0
   C eight and eight tenths, 9.21, 9.01
   Ⓓ eight and seventy-five hundredths, 8.80, 9.19

3. The length of New York's subway is 368 km, while the length of Moscow's subway is 306.2 km. Which subway system is longer? Use >, <, or = to compare the two lengths. Then justify your answer using place value.

   ## 368 > 306.2; New York's subway is longer.
   ## Check students' explanations.

4. In each box, write <, >, or = to make a true sentence:

   a. 46.491 ☐ 46.577   **b.** 2.15 ☐ 2.150   **c.** 11.341 ☐ 11.34
   (<)   **(=)**   **(>)**

   d. 0.495 ☐ 0.503   **e.** 0.080 ☐ 0.08   **f.** 8.70 ☐ 8.697
   (<)   **(=)**   **(>)**

page CC 13

---

5. Matt completed his first race in 15.163 seconds. The time of his second race was 15.24 seconds. Which of the following shows the correct relationship between 15.163 and 15.24?

   Ⓐ 15.163 < 15.24
   B 15.163 > 15.24
   C 15.24 < 15.163
   D 15.24 = 15.163

   Justify your answer.
   ## Check students' explanations.

6. Which of the following numbers is less than 23.90?

   A 23.9
   Ⓑ 23.09
   C 23.91
   D 23.92

7. Mrs Sanders bought 2 pumpkins. The first one weighed 4.89 kilograms; the second one weighed 4.9 kilograms. Use >, <, or = to compare the weights.

   ## 4.9 > 4.89, or 4.89 < 4.9
   Justify your answer.
   ## Check students' explanations.

8. Wendy, Todd, and Theresa went on a hike. They hiked 7.25 miles, 7.5 miles, and 7.245 miles. Order the distances from least to greatest.

   ## 7.245, 7.25, 7.5
   Justify your answer using place value.
   ## Check students' explanations.

page CC 14

Name _____

Common Core Standards Practice

5.NBT.4 Use place value understanding to round decimals to any place.

1. What is 5.385 rounded to the nearest tenth?

   A 5.3
   Ⓑ 5.4
   C 5.5
   D 5.6

2. What is 4.62 rounded to the nearest whole number?

   Ⓐ 5
   B 4.5
   C 4.7
   D 4.5

3. Round these numbers to the nearest tenth.

   a. 182.886 **182.9**   **d.** 7.96 **8.0**

   b. 0.459 **0.5**   **e.** 0.3 **0.3**

   c. 4.06 **4.1**   **f.** 3.21 **3.2**

4. Round these numbers to the nearest hundredth.

   a. 182.886 **182.89**   **d.** 8.31 **8.31**

   b. 0.459 **0.46**   **e.** 8.072 **8.07**

   c. 0.172 **0.17**   **f.** 130.039 **130.04**

page CC 15

---

5. Which of these numbers, when rounded to the nearest hundredth, is 0.05? Circle all that round to 0.05.

   (0.049)   0.057   (0.052)   0.44   0.55

6. What is 45.0189 rounded to the nearest thousandth?

   A 45.018
   B 45.0188
   Ⓒ 45.019
   D 45.0289

7. What is 4.106 rounded to the nearest hundredth?

   A 4.10
   Ⓑ 4.11
   C 4.12
   D 4.107

8. A box of uncooked spaghetti costs $0.1369 per ounce. How much is this cost to the nearest cent?
   ## $0.14

9. Roberto's baseball batting average is 0.278. What is his batting average rounded to the nearest hundredth?
   ## 0.28

10. Which of these numbers, when rounded to the nearest tenth, is 8.3? Circle all that round to 8.3.

    (8.28)   8.24   (8.33)   8.36   (8.25)

page CC 16

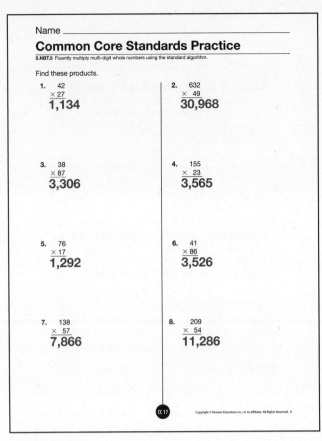

Common Core Standards Practice

5.NBT.5 Fluently multiply multi-digit whole numbers using the standard algorithm.

Find these products.

1. 42
    × 27
    1,134

2. 632
    × 49
    30,968

3. 38
    × 87
    3,306

4. 155
    × 23
    3,565

5. 76
    × 17
    1,292

6. 41
    × 86
    3,526

7. 138
    × 57
    7,866

8. 209
    × 54
    11,286

CC 17 Copyright © Pearson Education, Inc., or its affiliates. All Rights Reserved. 5

page CC 17

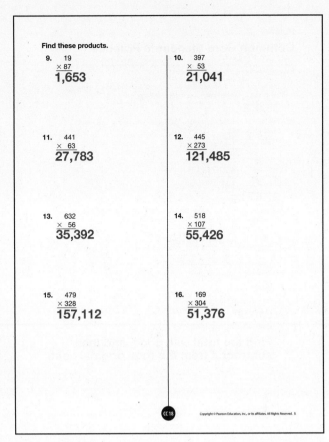

Find these products.

9. 19
    × 87
    1,653

10. 397
    × 53
    21,041

11. 441
    × 63
    27,783

12. 445
    × 273
    121,485

13. 632
    × 56
    35,392

14. 518
    × 107
    55,426

15. 479
    × 328
    157,112

16. 169
    × 304
    51,376

CC 18 Copyright © Pearson Education, Inc., or its affiliates. All Rights Reserved. 5

page CC 18

Common Core Standards Practice

5.NBT.6 Find whole-number quotients of whole numbers with up to four-digit dividends and two-digit divisors, using strategies based on place value, the properties of operations, and/or the relationship between multiplication and division. Illustrate and explain the calculation by using equations, rectangular arrays, and/or area models.

Solve these division problems.

1. 97)2,134
    22

2. 69)2,898
    42

3. A theater has 182 seats that are divided evenly into 14 rows. How many seats are in each row?

    a. Draw a model of the problem and write an equation that describes the model.

    Sample equation: 14 × S = 182. Check students' models.

    b. Solve the equation you wrote.

    There are 13 seats in each row.

4. Neil has 1,216 sports cards that he divides into 32 packages, each with the same number of cards. How many cards are in each package?

    a. Draw a model that represents this problem, and write an equation to match the model.

    Sample equation: 1,216 ÷ 32 = ? Models should suggest 32 packages with the same number of cards in each package.

    b. Solve the equation you wrote.

    There are 38 cards in each package.

CC 19 Copyright © Pearson Education, Inc., or its affiliates. All Rights Reserved. 5

page CC 19

Solve these division problems.

5. 68)1,904
    28

6. 57)5,415
    95

7. Marcia has 1,792 flowers for making centerpieces. Each centerpiece will have 64 flowers. How many centerpieces can she make?

    a. Draw a simple model that explains this problem, and write an equation that describes the model.

    Sample equation: 1,792 ÷ 64 = ? Models should suggest a group of 64 multiplied several times to make 1,792.

    b. Solve the equation you wrote.

    28 centerpieces

8. A plant nursery will plant 1,560 trees in ten different plots of land. Each plot of land will have the same number of trees, planted in rows of 12.

    a. How many trees will be planted in each plot of land?

    156 trees

    b. How many rows of trees will be on each plot of land?

    13 rows

    c. Justify your solutions using equations or models.

    Check students' work.

CC 20 Copyright © Pearson Education, Inc., or its affiliates. All Rights Reserved. 5

page CC 20

page CC 21

Name _____

Common Core Standards Practice

5.NBT.7 Add, subtract, multiply, and divide decimals to hundredths, using concrete models or drawings and strategies based on place value, properties of operations, and/or the relationship between addition and subtraction; relate the strategy to a written method and explain the reasoning used.

1. The temperature increased from 58.7°F to 92.6°F. Find the difference between the two temperatures in degrees Fahrenheit.

33.9°F

2. The table shows the mass of four packages. What is the total mass of the packages?

Package	Mass (kg)
1	3.94
2	14.81
3	11.27
4	7.65

37.67 kg

3. Alexandra went to the mall on Saturday and bought the items listed in the table. She bought each item at the discount price.

Item	Original Price ($)	Discount Price ($)
Bracelet	25.75	19.50
Hat	19.25	15.00

   a. What is the total cost of the items at their original prices?

   $45

   b. How much did Alexandra save?

   $10.50

   c. Explain how you determined how much she saved.

   Find the total sale price, and then subtract it from the total original cost.

page CC 22

4. A car gets 28.45 miles on 1 gallon of gasoline. The gasoline tank holds 11.5 gallons.

   a. Describe how to find how far the driver can drive the car on a full tank of gasoline.

   Multiply the distance it travels on 1 gallon, which is 28.45 miles, by the number of gallons in the tank.

   b. How far can the driver go in this car on a full tank?

   327.175 miles

5. Three stores sell Cactus Cola. The stores sell the same bottles, but they group them in packs of either 6, 12, or 24 bottles.

Store A	6-pack	$3.45
Store B	12-pack	$5.25
Store C	24-pack	$10.99

   a. How can you tell which store sells a bottle of cola for the lowest price?

   Divide the cost by the number of bottles in the pack.

   b. Which store sells Cactus cola bottles for the lowest price? What is this price?

   Store B, for $0.4375 per bottle

6. The table shows the admission price to a zoo.

Adult	$7.45
Student	$4.50
Child under 5	$3.75

   The Chung family buys 2 adult tickets, 2 student tickets, and 1 child's ticket. What is the total cost of the tickets?

   $27.65

page CC 23

Name _____

Common Core Standards Practice

5.NF.1 Add and subtract fractions with unlike denominators (including mixed numbers) by replacing given fractions with equivalent fractions in such a way as to produce an equivalent sum or difference of fractions with like denominators.

1. Which of these is equal to the sum of $\frac{4}{6}$ and $\frac{4}{9}$? Circle all that are equal to the sum.

   $\boxed{\frac{10}{9}}$ $\frac{8}{15}$ $\boxed{\frac{40}{36}}$ $\frac{4}{15}$ $\frac{11}{7}$ $\boxed{1\frac{2}{18}}$

2. Which of these is equal to the difference of $\frac{8}{9}$ and $\frac{2}{3}$? Circle all that are equal to the difference.

   $\frac{1}{12}$ $\boxed{\frac{2}{9}}$ $\frac{9}{14}$ $\frac{1}{9}$ $\boxed{\frac{4}{18}}$ $1\frac{5}{9}$

3. Which equivalent fractions can you use to find the sum of $\frac{2}{8} + \frac{3}{9}$?

   $\frac{18}{72}$ **and** $\frac{24}{72}$

4. Find the sum.

   $\frac{2}{8} + \frac{3}{9}$

   $\frac{7}{12}$

5. Which equivalent fractions can you use to find the difference of $5\frac{3}{12}$ and $1\frac{4}{9}$?

   $5\frac{9}{36}$ **and** $1\frac{16}{36}$

6. Find the difference.

   $5\frac{3}{12} - 1\frac{4}{9}$

   $3\frac{29}{36}$

page CC 24

7. Place these expressions in the appropriate column.

Less than 1	Equal to 1	Greater than 1
$\frac{1}{5} + \frac{3}{12}$	$\frac{3}{12} + \frac{3}{4}$	$\frac{1}{2} + \frac{5}{8}$
$3\frac{1}{4} - 2\frac{1}{2}$	$1\frac{4}{18} - \frac{2}{9}$	$3\frac{1}{3} - 1\frac{5}{6}$
$1\frac{1}{4} - \frac{9}{12}$		$\frac{7}{12} + \frac{2}{3}$

$\frac{1}{5} + \frac{3}{12}$ $3\frac{1}{4} - 2\frac{1}{2}$ $\frac{7}{12} + \frac{2}{3}$ $3\frac{1}{3} - 1\frac{5}{6}$

$1\frac{1}{4} - \frac{9}{12}$ $\frac{3}{12} + \frac{3}{4}$ $1\frac{4}{18} - \frac{2}{9}$ $\frac{1}{2} + \frac{5}{8}$

8. Which equivalent fractions can you use to find the sum of $2\frac{5}{6} + 1\frac{3}{4}$?

   $2\frac{10}{12}$ **and** $1\frac{9}{12}$

9. Find the sum.

   $2\frac{5}{6} + 1\frac{3}{4}$

   $4\frac{7}{12}$

10. Which equivalent fractions can you use to find the difference of $2\frac{5}{6}$ and $\frac{9}{5}$?

   $2\frac{25}{30}$ **and** $\frac{54}{30}$

11. Find the difference.

   $2\frac{5}{6} - \frac{9}{5}$

   $1\frac{1}{30}$

Name _____

Common Core Standards Practice

5.NF.2 Solve word problems involving addition and subtraction of fractions referring to the same whole, including cases of unlike denominators, e.g., by using visual fraction models or equations to represent the problem. Use benchmark fractions and number sense of fractions to estimate mentally and assess the reasonableness of answers.

1. Alex practices his guitar $\frac{5}{8}$ of an hour on Wednesday and $3\frac{3}{4}$ hours on Thursday.

   a. Write an equation that can be used to determine how many hours Alex practiced his guitar on Wednesday and Thursday.

   $$\frac{5}{8} + \frac{15}{4} = ?$$

   b. Solve the equation you wrote.

   $4\frac{3}{8}$ hours

2. Anna used $\frac{2}{5}$ yard of ribbon for one craft project and $\frac{3}{4}$ yard of ribbon for a second craft project.

   a. Estimate how much ribbon Anna used for the two projects.

   Check students' estimates. Answers should be about 1 yard.

   b. Use the number line to model the problem situation.

   c. How much ribbon did Anna use for the two craft projects?

   $1\frac{3}{20}$ yards

page CC 25

---

3. Maria bought $1\frac{1}{2}$ pounds of nails for a carpentry project. She ended up with $\frac{3}{8}$ pound of nails when she finished the project.

   a. Write an equation that can be used to determine how much of the $1\frac{1}{2}$ pounds of nails Maria used.

   $$\frac{3}{2} - \frac{3}{8} = ?$$

   b. Solve the equation you wrote.

   $1\frac{1}{8}$ pounds

4. Jack ran $\frac{2}{8}$ mile and Roy ran $\frac{2}{3}$ mile.

   a. What benchmark fractions can be used to estimate how much farther Roy ran than Jack?

   $\frac{1}{4}$ for $\frac{2}{8}$ and $\frac{3}{4}$ for $\frac{2}{3}$

   b. Using the benchmark fractions, what is a reasonable estimate for the difference between the two distances?

   $\frac{1}{2}$ mile

   c. What is the actual difference?

   $\frac{5}{12}$ mile

5. Eva's new dog weighed $5\frac{7}{8}$ pounds when she first got him 4 weeks ago. Now he weighs $12\frac{1}{4}$ pounds.

   a. Eva thinks that her dog has gained 6 pounds since she got him. Is her estimate reasonable?

   Check students' answers. Sample answer: Yes, 6 is a reasonable estimate. $5\frac{7}{8}$ is about 6 pounds, $12\frac{1}{4}$ is about 12 pounds.

   b. How much weight has Eva's dog actually gained?

   $6\frac{3}{8}$ pounds

page CC 26

Name _____

Common Core Standards Practice

5.NF.3 Interpret a fraction as division of the numerator by the denominator ($\frac{a}{b} = a \div b$). Solve word problems involving division of whole numbers leading to answers in the form of fractions or mixed numbers, e.g., by using visual fraction models or equations to represent the problem.

1. Which division expression matches the model?

   A $3 \div 4$ **C** $3 \div 2$
   B $2 \div 3$ **D** $4 \div 2$

2. Which model matches the division expression?

   $6 \div 4$

3. a. Use the bar model below to show 8 bars divided evenly into 5 parts.

   b. Is each part bigger or smaller than the individual bars? Explain how you know.

   Each part is bigger than the individual bars. Check students' explanations.

4. a. Use the bar model below to show 5 bars divided evenly into 8 parts.

   b. Is each part bigger or smaller than the individual bars? Explain how you know.

   Each part is smaller than the individual bars. Check students' explanations.

page CC 27

---

5. Eva has 35 apples. She divides them equally into 7 bags. Which fraction represents the number of apples Eva puts in each bag?

   A $\frac{35}{7}$
   B $\frac{7}{35}$
   C $\frac{35}{5}$
   D $\frac{28}{35}$

6. Beth has 8 acres of land. She wants to grow 5 types of crops, each on the same size plot.

   a. Write a division statement to represent the number of acres of land for each crop.

   $8 \div 5$

   b. Write your answer as a mixed number.

   $1\frac{3}{5}$

7. Ms. George baked 2 cakes of equal size. Each of her 12 guests ate the same amount of cake, and no cake was left over.

   a. What fraction of a cake did each guest eat?

   $\frac{2}{12}$, or $\frac{1}{6}$, of a cake

   b. How do you think Ms. George cut the cakes into equal pieces? Explain.

   She may have cut each cake into 6 equal pieces. This would make 12 total pieces of cake, or 1 piece for each guest.

8. Allen bought a 15-pound bag of ice. He distributed the ice evenly among 4 coolers. How many pounds of ice went into each cooler? Express your answer as a mixed number.

   $3\frac{3}{4}$ pounds

page CC 28

Common Core Standards Practice

5.NF.4a Apply and extend previous understandings of multiplication to multiply a fraction or whole number by a fraction. Interpret the product ($\frac{a}{b}$) × q as a parts of a partition of q into b equal parts; equivalently, as the result of a sequence of operations a × q ÷ b.

1. A baker uses $\frac{2}{3}$ of a stick of butter to make one batch of cookies. How many sticks of butter does she need to make 3 batches of cookies?

   a. The model below represents the problem situation. Explain the model.

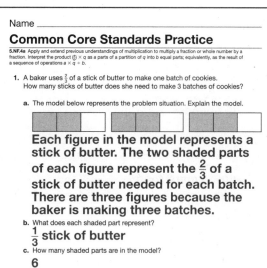

Each figure in the model represents a stick of butter. The two shaded parts of each figure represent the $\frac{2}{3}$ of a stick of butter needed for each batch. There are three figures because the baker is making three batches.

   b. What does each shaded part represent?

$\frac{1}{3}$ stick of butter

   c. How many shaded parts are in the model?

6

   d. Write an expression that can be used to determine how many sticks of butter the baker needs.

$\frac{2}{3} \times 3$

   e. How much butter does the baker need for three batches of cookies?

2 sticks of butter

2. Use the model below to show $\frac{2}{5} \times 4$.

CC 29   Copyright © Pearson Education, Inc., or its affiliates. All Rights Reserved. 5

page CC 29

---

3. Explain why $2 \times \frac{3}{8}$ is equivalent to $2 \times 3 \times \frac{1}{8}$.

Check students' explanations. They should explain that $\frac{3}{8}$ is the same as $3 \times \frac{1}{8}$.

4. Match the model with the expression.

$\frac{2}{9} \times 3$

$4 \times \frac{1}{3}$

$\frac{3}{4} \times 2$

$5 \times \frac{1}{2}$

5. Draw a model to show $\frac{1}{4} \times \frac{2}{3}$. Then find the product.

$\frac{2}{12} = \frac{1}{6}$

6. Draw a model to show $5 \times \frac{4}{5}$. Then find the product.

4

CC 30   Copyright © Pearson Education, Inc., or its affiliates. All Rights Reserved. 5

page CC 30

Common Core Standards Practice

5.NF.4b Apply and extend previous understandings of multiplication to multiply a fraction or whole number by a fraction. Find the area of a rectangle with fractional side lengths by tiling it with unit squares of the appropriate unit fraction side lengths, and show that the area is the same as would be found by multiplying the side lengths. Multiply fractional side lengths to find areas of rectangles, and represent fraction products as rectangular areas.

For 1–4, write an equation to find the area of the shaded rectangles. Then solve the equation.

1.

$\frac{1}{2} \times \frac{3}{4} = \frac{3}{8}$

2.

$\frac{3}{4} \times \frac{2}{5} = \frac{6}{20}$

3.

$\frac{3}{5} \times \frac{3}{6} = \frac{9}{30}$

4.

$\frac{2}{3} \times \frac{1}{4} = \frac{2}{12}$

5. Angie got a new area rug for her room. The figure on the right shows the dimensions of her room and the area rug.

   a. What are the dimensions of the area rug?

    Width: **4 feet**

    Length: **$5\frac{1}{2}$ feet**

   b. What is the area of the area rug?

   22 square feet

CC 31   Copyright © Pearson Education, Inc., or its affiliates. All Rights Reserved. 5

page CC 31

---

6. What is the area of a rectangle with length 5 feet and width $6\frac{1}{2}$ feet?

   A 30 ft²

   B $30\frac{1}{2}$ ft²

   C $34\frac{1}{2}$ ft²

   D $32\frac{1}{2}$ ft²

7. What is the area of a rectangle that is $8\frac{2}{5}$ inches long and 6 inches wide?

   A $5\frac{2}{5}$ in.²

   B $48\frac{2}{5}$ in.²

   C $50\frac{2}{5}$ in.²

   D $100\frac{4}{5}$ in.²

8. Find the area of a rectangle that is $6\frac{1}{3}$ inches long and $4\frac{3}{4}$ inches wide.

$30\frac{1}{12}$ square inches

9. Jay arranges 18 feet of fencing into a rectangle that is 5 feet long and 4 feet wide. Show that he could make a larger area by arranging the fencing into a square.

The area of the rectangle is 5 ft × 4 ft = 20 square feet. By arranging the fence into a square of side length $4\frac{1}{2}$ feet, the area becomes $20\frac{1}{4}$ square feet.

10. John has a rectangular patio that is $6\frac{3}{4}$ yards long and $4\frac{1}{3}$ yards wide. What is the area of the patio?

$29\frac{1}{4}$ yd²

CC 32   Copyright © Pearson Education, Inc., or its affiliates. All Rights Reserved. 5

page CC 32

Page CC 33

Common Core Standards Practice

5.NF.5a Interpret multiplication as scaling (resizing) by: Comparing the size of a product to the size of one factor on the basis of the size of the other factor, without performing the indicated multiplication.

1. Write the expressions in the appropriate place. You should NOT find the products of the expressions.

Less than 5	Equal to 5	Greater than 5
$5 \times \frac{2}{3}$	$\frac{1}{2} \times 10$	$5 \times \frac{3}{2}$
$\frac{1}{2} \times 5$	$\frac{3}{3} \times 5$	$5 \times \frac{4}{3}$
$\frac{7}{8} \times 5$	$5 \times \frac{4}{4}$	

$5 \times \frac{3}{2}$ $\qquad$ $5 \times \frac{2}{3}$ $\qquad$ $5 \times \frac{4}{3}$ $\qquad$ $\frac{1}{2} \times 10$

$\frac{1}{2} \times 5$ $\qquad$ $\frac{3}{3} \times 5$ $\qquad$ $\frac{7}{8} \times 5$ $\qquad$ $5 \times \frac{4}{4}$

2. For each statement 2a through 2d, circle YES if the statement is true or NO if the statement is not true.

a. $\frac{3}{5} \times 5 > 5$ $\qquad$ YES (NO)

b. $\frac{3}{5} \times 5 > \frac{3}{5}$ $\qquad$ (YES) NO

c. $6 \times \frac{3}{2} > 6$ $\qquad$ (YES) NO

d. $6 \times \frac{3}{2} < \frac{3}{2}$ $\qquad$ YES (NO)

page CC 33

Page CC 34

3. Jeff feeds the family dog on Wednesdays and his sister Melody feeds the dog on Fridays. On Wednesday, Jeff gave the dog $\frac{5}{8}$ of an 8-ounce can of dog food. On Friday, Melody, gave the dog $\frac{1}{2}$ of an 8-ounce can of dog food.

a. Write an expression that can be use to determine how many ounces of dog food Jeff fed the dog on Wednesday.

$$\frac{5}{8} \times 8$$

b. Write an expression that can be use to determine how many ounces of dog food Melody fed the dog on Friday.

$$\frac{1}{2} \times 8$$

c. Who gave the dog more food, Jeff or Melody? Explain your answer.

Jeff gave the dog more food. $\frac{5}{8}$ of an 8-ounce can is more than $\frac{1}{2}$ of an 8-ounce can.

4. For each statement 4a through 4d, circle YES if the statement is true or NO if the statement is not true.

a. $\frac{5}{2} \times 3 > 3$ $\qquad$ (YES) NO

b. $\frac{5}{2} \times 3 < \frac{5}{2}$ $\qquad$ YES (NO)

c. $10 \times \frac{4}{5} < 10$ $\qquad$ (YES) NO

d. $10 \times \frac{4}{5} > \frac{4}{5}$ $\qquad$ (YES) NO

5. For each pair of expressions, circle the greater product without finding the product.

a. $\boxed{\frac{3}{4} \times \frac{3}{2}}$ and $\frac{3}{4} \times \frac{1}{2}$

b. $\frac{2}{3} \times 3\frac{1}{4}$ and $\boxed{\frac{4}{3} \times 3\frac{1}{4}}$

c. $\frac{3}{8} \times \frac{3}{8}$ and $\boxed{\frac{3}{8} \times \frac{1}{2}}$

page CC 34

Page CC 35

Common Core Standards Practice

5.NF.5b Interpret multiplication as scaling (resizing) by: Explaining why multiplying a given number by a fraction greater than 1 results in a product greater than the given number (recognizing multiplication by whole numbers greater than 1 as a familiar case); explaining why multiplying a given number by a fraction less than 1 results in a product smaller than the given number; and relating the principle of fraction equivalence $\frac{a}{b} = \frac{(n \times a)}{(n \times b)}$ to the effect of multiplying $\frac{a}{b}$ by 1.

1. Sam buys two carpets. One carpet is 3 feet by $\frac{7}{8}$ foot. The other carpet is 3 feet by $\frac{3}{4}$ foot.

a. Which carpet has the greater area? Explain how you can find the answer without calculating either area.

The $3 \times \frac{7}{8}$ carpet has a greater area because $\frac{7}{8}$ is greater than $\frac{3}{4}$.

b. Which carpet has an area less than 3 square feet? How do you know?

The $3 \times \frac{3}{4}$ carpet; multiplying by a fraction less than 1 results in a number less than the given number.

2. Jasmine tapes together 3 straws in a straight line. Each straw is $9\frac{1}{2}$ inches long. To find the total length of the straws, Jasmine multiplies $9\frac{1}{2}$ by $\frac{3}{3}$.

a. Describe the error Jasmine made.

Jasmine should have multiplied by 3, not $\frac{3}{3}$.

b. What is the value of the product that Jasmine found? Explain.

$9\frac{1}{2}$; the fraction $\frac{3}{3}$ is equal to 1, and multiplying a number by 1 does not change its value.

3. Explain why the product of 9 and $\frac{2}{3}$ is less than 9.

Possible answer: multiplying 9 and $\frac{2}{3}$ is the same as adding 9 values of $\frac{2}{3}$ together. Since $\frac{2}{3}$ is less than 1, 9 of them will be less than 9.

page CC 35

Page CC 36

4. The model shows three equal mixed numbers.

a. Write the product that the model represents.

$$3 \times 2\frac{3}{4}$$

b. How does the model show that the product is greater than 8?

Two pieces from the last circle can fill in the missing pieces from the other two circles. This will create 8 full circles, plus some left over.

5. Explain why the product of 12 and $\frac{3}{2}$ is greater than 12.

Possible answer: Multiplying 12 and $\frac{3}{2}$ is the same as adding 12 values of $\frac{3}{2}$ together. Since $\frac{3}{2}$ is greater than 1, 12 of them will be greater than 12.

6. The equation shows two equivalent fractions.

$$\frac{8 \times ?}{10 \times ?} = \frac{48}{60}$$

a. What is the value of the question mark in the equation?

6

b. How do you know that $\frac{8}{10}$ and $\frac{48}{60}$ are equivalent?

Multiplying by $\frac{6}{6}$, which is equal to 1, does not change the value of the fraction.

c. Write another fraction that is equal to $\frac{8}{10}$.

Possible answer: $\frac{16}{20}$

page CC 36

Name _____

Common Core Standards Practice

5.NF.6 Solve real world problems involving multiplication of fractions and mixed numbers, e.g., by using visual fraction models or equations to represent the problem.

1. Mato's marinara recipe calls for $\frac{3}{4}$ tablespoon of tomato paste. He plans to make 12 batches of marinara. How much tomato paste will Mato need?

   a. Draw a model to represent the problem situation. Then find the solution.

   9 tablespoons; check students' models.

2. John is training for a bicycle race. This week he rode his bicycle a total of 13 miles. Next week he plans to ride $2\frac{1}{2}$ times as far. How many miles will John ride his bicycle next week? Write an equation to represent the problem situation. Then solve the equation.

   $13 \times 2\frac{1}{2} = 32\frac{1}{2}$ **miles**

page CC 37

---

3. It snowed $37\frac{3}{4}$ inches last winter, which was 2 times more snow than the average. What is the average snow fall?

   a. Write an equation that matches the problem situation. Then solve the equation.

   $x \times 2 = 37\frac{3}{4}; x = 18\frac{7}{8}$

4. Alan's cake recipe requires $3\frac{2}{3}$ cups of flour. Alan is making 6 cakes. How much flour does he need?

   a. Draw a model to represent the problem situation.

   Check students' models.

   b. Write an equation to match the model you drew. Then solve the equation.

   $6 \times 3\frac{2}{3}$; **22 cups**

5. Julia and Awan are making a retangular banner. The banner will be $4\frac{1}{4}$ feet by $2\frac{3}{4}$ feet. What will be the area of the banner?

   $4\frac{1}{4} \times 2\frac{3}{4} = 11\frac{11}{16}$ **square feet**

page CC 38

Name _____

Common Core Standards Practice

5.NF.7a Apply and extend previous understandings of division to divide unit fractions by whole numbers and whole numbers by unit fractions. Interpret division of a unit fraction by a non-zero whole number, and compute such quotients.

1. Five friends will share equally $\frac{1}{2}$ yard of felt for an art project. How much felt will each friend get?

   a. Use the model to represent the problem situation.

   b. Describe in words what the model shows.

   a $\frac{1}{2}$-yard piece of felt divided into 5 pieces

   c. Write and solve an equation that matches the model.

   $\frac{1}{2} \div 5 = \frac{1}{10}$

2. A farmer will divide a $\frac{1}{4}$-acre plot of land into three equal-sized sections. What will be the size of each section?

   a. Use the model to represent the problem situation.

   b. Describe in words what the model shows.

   a $\frac{1}{4}$-acre plot of land into three equal-sized sections

   c. Write and solve an equation that matches the model.

   $\frac{1}{4} \div 3 = \frac{1}{12}$

page CC 39

---

3. Which of these models show $\frac{1}{5} \div 6$? Circle all that apply.

4. a. Describe a problem situation to match the equation below.

   $\frac{1}{3} \div 7 = \square$

   Check students' problem situations. Sample answer: Seven students will divide evenly $\frac{1}{3}$ yard of ribbon.

   b. Draw a model to represent the problem situation.

   Check students' models.

   c. Write and solve an equation that matches the model.

   $\frac{1}{3} \div 7 = \frac{1}{21}$

page CC 40

page CC 41

Name _____

Common Core Standards Practice

5.NF.7b Apply and extend previous understandings of division to divide unit fractions by whole numbers and whole numbers by unit fractions. Interpret division of a whole number by a unit fraction, and compute such quotients.

1. How many $\frac{1}{2}$-pound pieces are in a 3-pound piece of cheese?

   a. Complete the model to represent the problem situation.

   1 lb   2 lb   3 lb

   b. Describe in words what the model shows.

   a 3-pound piece of cheese divided into $\frac{1}{2}$-pound pieces

   c. Write and solve an equation to match the model.

   $3 \div \frac{1}{2} = 6$

2. How many $\frac{1}{4}$-mile segments are in a 2-mile relay?

   a. Complete the model to represent the problem situation.

   0   1   2

   b. Describe in words what the model shows.

   a distance of 2 miles divided into $\frac{1}{4}$-mile segments

   c. Write and solve an equation that matches the model.

   $2 \div \frac{1}{4} = 8$

page CC 42

3. a. Describe a problem situation that matches this model.

   1   2   3   4   5

   Check student's answers.

   b. Write and solve an equation to match the model.

   $5 \div \frac{1}{8} = 40$

4. Match the model to the expression. Not all expressions match a model. Not all models match an expression.

   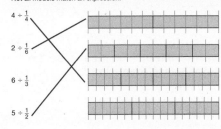

   $4 \div \frac{1}{4}$

   $2 \div \frac{1}{6}$

   $6 \div \frac{1}{3}$

   $5 \div \frac{1}{2}$

page CC 43

Name _____

Common Core Standards Practice

5.NF.7c Apply and extend previous understandings of division to divide unit fractions by whole numbers and whole numbers by unit fractions. Solve real world problems involving division of unit fractions by non-zero whole numbers and division of whole numbers by unit fractions, e.g., by using visual fraction models and equations to represent the problem.

1. Jimmy buys 3 whole pizzas. Each slice is $\frac{1}{8}$ of a pizza. How many slices are in all 3 pizzas?

   Ⓐ 24

   B $\frac{1}{24}$

   C 32

   D $\frac{1}{32}$

2. Jack buys a bag of 5 apples, each equal in size. He eats $\frac{1}{2}$ of one apple. What fraction of the bag of apples did he eat?

   A 5

   Ⓑ $\frac{1}{10}$

   C $\frac{1}{2}$

   D $\frac{2}{5}$

3. Jonny uses $\frac{1}{5}$ of a jar of dressing on 4 servings of salad. He uses an equal amount of dressing on each serving.

   a. Write an equation that can be used to determine the fraction of the jar of dressing that he uses on each serving.

   $\frac{1}{5} \div 4 = ?$

   b. Solve the equation you wrote.

   $\frac{1}{20}$ **of a jar**

4. Debbi spent a total of 6 hours decorating her classroom. She worked in sessions that each lasted $\frac{1}{3}$ hour.

   a. Write an equation that can be used to determine how many sessions Debbi needed.

   $6 \div \frac{1}{3} = ?$

   b. Solve the equation you wrote.
   18 sessions

page CC 44

5. Barry buys a plot of land that measures $\frac{1}{2}$ acre. He divides the plot into 5 equal pieces.

   a. Draw a model to illustrate the problem.
   Check students' models.

   b. What fraction of an acre is each piece?
   $\frac{1}{10}$ **acre**

6. A turtle walks at an average speed of $\frac{1}{3}$ mile per hour.

   a. Write an equation that can be used to find how long it would take the turtle to walk 2 miles.

   $2 \div \frac{1}{3} = ?$

   b. Solve the equation you wrote.
   6 hours

7. Mr. Smith has 7 cups of raisins. He likes to add $\frac{1}{4}$ cup of raisins to a bowl of cereal.

   a. Write an equation that can be used to determine how many bowls of cereal Mr. Smith can supply with raisins.

   $7 \div \frac{1}{4} = ?$

   b. Solve the equation you wrote.
   28 bowls

8. a. Draw a model to illustrate the division problem $\frac{1}{5} \div 3$.
   Check students' models.

   b. Find the quotient. $\frac{1}{15}$

Common Core Standards Practice

5.MD.1 Convert among different-sized standard measurement units within a given measurement system (e.g., convert 5 cm to 0.05 m), and use these conversions in solving multi-step, real world problems.

1. How many kilometers equal 1,200 meters?

   A 0.12
   B 1.2 (circled)
   C 12
   D 120

2. How many pints are in 5.5 gallons?

   A 22
   B 33
   C 44 (circled)
   D 55

3. Polly measures the height of a bookcase to be 2 feet, 10 inches.

  a. What is the height of the bookcase in inches?

34 inches

  b. Is the height of the bookcase less than, equal to, or greater than 1 yard? Explain how you know.

1 yard = 3 feet = 36 inches, so the height is less than 1 yard.

4. Carl ran 120 feet, while his friend Eva ran 25 yards.

  a. Express 25 yards in feet.

25 yards = 75 feet.

  b. Express 120 feet in yards.

120 feet = 40 yards.

page CC 45

---

5. Which measurements are equal to 12 feet? Circle all that apply.

60 inches   **4 yards** (circled)   108 inches   3 yards

2 yards   120 inches   6 yards   **144 inches** (circled)

6. Which measurements are equal to 66 meters? Circle all that apply.

330 cm   3,300 cm   33,000 mm   0.33 km

0.66 km   **6,600 cm** (circled)   660 cm   **66,000 mm** (circled)

7. Jan's puppy has a mass of 3.9 kg. Alice's puppy has a mass of 2,750 g.

  a. Write the mass of Alice's puppy in kilograms.

2.75 kg

  b. Whose puppy has a greater mass? Explain how you know.

Jan's puppy; 3.9 is greater than 2.75.

8. Mike buys 4.5 meters of ribbon for a party.

  a. What is the length of the ribbon in centimeters?

450 centimeters

  b. What is the length of the ribbon in millimeters?

4,500 millimeters

page CC 46

Common Core Standards Practice

5.MD.2 Make a line plot to display a data set of measurements in fractions of a unit $(\frac{1}{2}, \frac{1}{4}, \frac{1}{8})$. Use operations on fractions for this grade to solve problems involving information presented in line plots.

A teacher asked students to write the total number of hours that they each spent studying math and doing math homework in the last week. She recorded the data in a table.

Hours Spent on Math Last Week

$1\frac{1}{2}$	$1\frac{3}{4}$	$1\frac{1}{4}$	$2\frac{1}{4}$	$3\frac{1}{4}$	$\frac{3}{4}$	$2\frac{1}{2}$	$3\frac{3}{4}$	$5\frac{1}{4}$	$3\frac{1}{2}$	$4\frac{1}{4}$	$2\frac{1}{4}$
$3\frac{1}{2}$	$2\frac{3}{4}$	$2\frac{1}{2}$	$4\frac{3}{4}$	$3\frac{1}{2}$	$2\frac{1}{4}$	$3\frac{1}{4}$	$2\frac{3}{4}$	$2\frac{1}{4}$	$1\frac{3}{4}$	$3\frac{3}{4}$	$3\frac{1}{2}$

1. Make a line plot of this data.

2. How much longer was the greatest amount of time spent than the least amount of time spent on math last week?

$4\frac{1}{2}$ hours

3. How many times greater was the greatest amount of time spent than the least amount of time spent on math last week?

7 times greater

4. What were the two most common number of hours spent on math last week? What is the difference between those times?

$3\frac{1}{2}$ hours and $2\frac{1}{4}$ hours; $1\frac{1}{4}$ hours

page CC 47

The students in two fifth grade classes recorded the number of miles they walked for the charity walk.

Miles Walked

2	$1\frac{3}{4}$	$2\frac{3}{4}$	$2\frac{1}{4}$	3	$3\frac{1}{4}$	$3\frac{1}{2}$	$3\frac{3}{4}$	4	$4\frac{1}{4}$	$4\frac{1}{2}$	$2\frac{1}{4}$
$6\frac{1}{2}$	$6\frac{1}{4}$	$3\frac{1}{2}$	4	$4\frac{1}{2}$	$4\frac{1}{4}$	$5\frac{1}{2}$	$4\frac{1}{4}$	6	3	$3\frac{3}{4}$	4
$4\frac{1}{4}$	$5\frac{1}{2}$	5	4	$3\frac{1}{2}$	$4\frac{1}{4}$	6	8	$5\frac{3}{4}$	$7\frac{1}{2}$	$5\frac{1}{2}$	$7\frac{1}{4}$

5. Make a line plot of the data.

6. What was the greatest difference between the number of miles walked by any two students?

$6\frac{1}{4}$ miles

7. Of the group of students who each walked $4\frac{1}{4}$ miles, how many miles did they walk in all?

$21\frac{1}{4}$ miles

8. Lisa and Jorge walked the second and third most miles. How many miles did Lisa and Jorge walk combined?

$14\frac{3}{4}$ miles

page CC 48

Page CC 49

Name _____

Common Core Standards Practice

5.MD.3ab Recognize volume as an attribute of solid figures and understand concepts of volume measurement. A cube with side length 1 unit, called a "unit cube," is said to have "one cubic unit" of volume, and can be used to measure volume. A solid figure which can be packed without gaps or overlaps using n unit cubes is said to have a volume of n cubic units.

1. Which of these describes a measure of volume? Circle all that apply.

the height of a wall   the number of tiles that cover a floor

the distance around a yard   (the number of packing peanuts in a box)

(the amount of crushed rock   the amount of yard a garden takes up
that fills a hole)

2. Janelle has a large supply of small cubes, each the same size. How could she use the cubes to measure the volume of a shoebox?

She could count the number of cubes that fit inside the shoebox.

3. Bill arranges 50 small cubes in a 5-by-10 array along a bookshelf. He claims that the volume of books that the shelf can hold is equal to 50 cubic units. Is his claim correct? If not, explain how he could find the volume.

The claim is not correct. He found the area of the shelf, not the volume. He could find the volume by piling cubes into the space on the shelf that books would fill.

page CC 49

Page CC 50

4. Gill creates a model prism using 22 unit cubes. What is the volume of the prism?

   A 11 units
   B 22 units
   C 22 cubic units ⟵ circled
   D 66 cubic units

5. A box has a volume of 64 cubic units. How many cubes with a volume of 1 cubic unit can fit in the box?

   A 4
   B 8
   C 16
   D 64 ⟵ circled

6. Walter's father put mulch around some trees in the yard. Walter measured the depth of the mulch. He found that there was 2 inches of mulch around each tree. Does the measurement of 2 inches show exactly how much mulch Walter's father used around each tree? Explain why or why not.

No. He would need to find the volume, so in addition to the depth, Walter would need the area of the mulched space around the trees.

7. A closet measures 5 feet wide and 3 feet deep. Does the measurement of 15 square feet show the volume inside the closet? If not, how could you find the volume inside the closet?

No. The area of the floor is 15 square feet. The volume is the amount of space inside the closet. I can find the volume of the closet by filling it with cube-shaped boxes that are the same size.

page CC 50

Page CC 51

Name _____

Common Core Standards Practice

5.MD.4 Measure volumes by counting unit cubes, using cubic cm, cubic in, cubic ft, and improvised units.

Count the cubes to determine the volume of each shape. There are no hidden cubes.

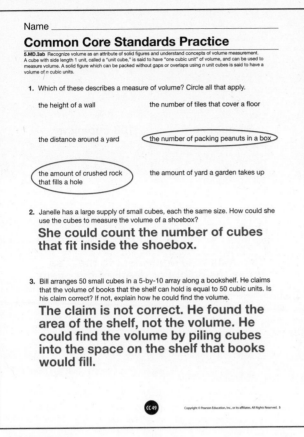

1. A 10 cubic units
   B 9 cubic units ⟵ circled
   C 12 cubic units
   D 5 cubic units

2. A 10 cubic units
   B 5 cubic units
   C 8 cubic units ⟵ circled
   D 5 cubic units

3. A 6 cubic units ⟵ circled
   B 8 cubic units
   C 12 cubic units
   D 15 cubic units

4. A 6 cubic units
   B 9 cubic units
   C 10 cubic units
   D 15 cubic units ⟵ circled

page CC 51

Page CC 52

In these shapes, the volume of each cube is 1 cubic centimeters. Find the volume of each shape in cubic centimeters.

5. **25 cubic centimeters**

6. **24 cubic centimeters**

7. **21 cubic centimeters**

8. **15 cubic centimeters**

9. **24 cubic centimeters**

10. **20 cubic centimeters**

page CC 52

page CC 53

Name _____

Common Core Standards Practice

5.MD.5a Relate volume to the operations of multiplication and addition and solve real world and mathematical problems involving volume. Find the volume of a right rectangular prism with whole-number side lengths by packing it with unit cubes, and show that the volume is the same as would be found by multiplying the edge lengths, equivalently by multiplying the height by the area of the base. Represent threefold whole-number products as volumes, e.g., to represent the associative property of multiplication.

Find the volumes of the rectangular prisms shown below.

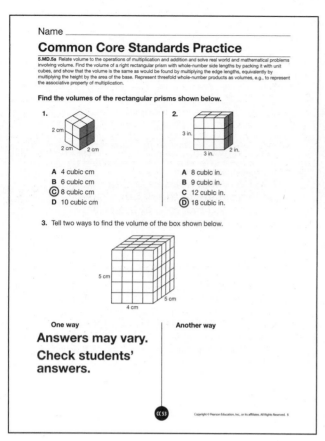

1.

2 cm, 2 cm, 2 cm

A 4 cubic cm
B 6 cubic cm
Ⓒ 8 cubic cm
D 10 cubic cm

2.

3 in., 3 in., 2 in.

A 8 cubic in.
B 9 cubic in.
C 12 cubic in.
Ⓓ 18 cubic in.

3. Tell two ways to find the volume of the box shown below.

5 cm, 5 cm, 4 cm

One way

Answers may vary. Check students' answers.

Another way

page CC 54

4. Find the volume for each of these rectangular prisms.

3 cm, 4 cm, 7 cm

a. **84 cubic cm**

3 cm, 4 cm, 9 cm

b. **108 cubic cm**

4 in., 4 in., 4 in.

c. **64 cubic in.**

2 in., 8 in., 2 in.

d. **32 cubic in.**

5. How does knowing the area of one face of a prism help you find the volume of the prism?

The volume is equivalent to the area times the height or depth of the prism.

page CC 55

Name _____

Common Core Standards Practice

5. MD.5b Relate volume to the operations of multiplication and addition and solve real world and mathematical problems involving volume. Apply the formulas $V = l \times w \times h$ and $V = b \times h$ for rectangular prisms to find volumes of right rectangular prisms with whole-number edge lengths in the context of solving real world and mathematical problems.

1. A milk carton is in the shape of a rectangular prism that is 6 inches long, 4 inches wide, and 4 inches tall. What is its volume?

96 cubic inches

2. A room is in the shape of a rectangular prism that is 13 feet long, 10 feet high, and 11 feet wide. What is its volume?

1,430 cubic feet

3. A bank vault is in the shape of a rectangular prism with a floor area of 280 square feet and a height of 19 feet. Calculate its volume.

5,320 cubic feet

4. Calculate the volume of the jewelry box shown below.

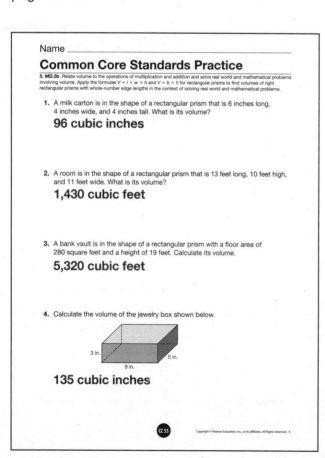

3 in., 9 in., 5 in.

135 cubic inches

page CC 56

5. A dumpster is in the shape of a rectangular prism. Its base measures 136 square feet, and its height is 6 feet. What is the volume of the dumpster?

816 cubic feet

6. The antique bottle shown below consists of a rectangular prism and a cylinder-shaped spout. Find the volume of the prism section of the bottle.

6 in., 4 in., 3 in.

72 cubic inches

7. Kyle will fill the candle mold shown below with liquid wax. Find the amount of liquid wax that the mold can hold.

11 in., 3 in., 3 in.

99 cubic inches

8. Victor keeps a rabbit in a cage that has the shape of a rectangular prism. The ends of the cage measures 4 square feet and the cage is 3 feet long. What is the volume of the cage?

12 cubic feet

page CC 57

Name _____

Common Core Standards Practice

5. MD.5c Relate volume to the operations of multiplication and addition and solve real world and mathematical problems involving volume. Recognize volume as additive. Find volumes of solid figures composed of two non-overlapping right rectangular prisms by adding the volumes of the non-overlapping parts, applying this technique to solve real world problems.

Find the volume of each individual prism. Then add the volumes to find the volume of the combined prisms.

1.

___50___ cubic inches + ___25___ cubic inches = ___75___ cubic inches

2.

___24___ cubic meters + ___72___ cubic meters = ___96___ cubic meters

page CC 58

Find the volume of these shapes. Each was made by joining two rectangular prisms together.

3.

220 yd³

4.

150 in.³

5.

140 ft³

6.

52 in.³

7. A moving truck has a floor space that is 14 feet long, 8 feet wide, and 9 feet tall. The truck also has an additional space at the front of the truck that is 3 feet long, 4 feet tall, and the same width as the rest of the truck. How much space is there inside the moving truck?

1,104 ft³

page CC 59

Name _____

Common Core Standards Practice

5.G.1 Use a pair of perpendicular number lines, called axes, to define a coordinate system, with the intersection of the lines (the origin) arranged to coincide with the 0 on each line and a given point in the plane located by using an ordered pair of numbers, called its coordinates. Understand that the first number indicates how far to travel from the origin in the direction of one axis, and the second number indicates how far to travel in the direction of the second axis, with the convention that the names of the two axes and the coordinates correspond (e.g., x-axis and x-coordinate, y-axis and y-coordinate).

Use the coordinate plane below for Exercises 1–3.

1. Label these parts of the coordinate plane.
   a. x-axis
   b. y-axis
   c. O

2. Draw and label a line to show where the x-coordinate is always equal to 6.

   See vertical line on coordinate plane.

3. Draw and label a line to show where the y-coordinate is always equal to 3.

   See horizontal line on coordinate plane.

page CC 60

Use the coordinate plane below to find the point that matches each description. Name each point with a letter and its coordinates.

4. the point on the x-axis ___**C (4, 0)**___

5. the point on the y-axis ___**A (0, 3)**___

6. the point that has an x-coordinate of 7 ___**D (7, 3)**___

7. the point that has a y-coordinate of 7 ___**B (2, 7)**___

8. the point that has x- and y-coordinates that equal each other ___**E (8, 8)**___

page CC 61

Name _____

Common Core Standards Practice

5.G.2 Represent real world and mathematical problems by graphing points in the first quadrant of the coordinate plane, and interpret coordinate values of points in the context of the situation.

1. Write the coordinates for the points shown in the coordinate plane.

A(**1** , **3**)   D(**6** , **8**)
B(**3** , **4**)   E(**9** , **5**)
C(**5** , **1**)   F(**8** , **0**)

2. Graph and label these points in the coordinate plane.

A(3, 4)   D(8, 9)

B(5, 5)   E(2, 8)

C(7, 2)   F(0, 5)

page CC 62

3. Downtown has streets and avenues that fit the coordinate plane, as shown in the map below.

Legend:
- 🚕 Taxi stand
- $ Bank
- ✚ Hospital
- ● Hotel
- ■ Office Tower
- ▲ Theater

The taxi stand is at the corner of 1ˢᵗ Street and 5ᵗʰ Avenue.

Name the locations of the other places.

a. Hotel: **2ⁿᵈ Street, 3ʳᵈ Avenue**

b. Bank: **5ᵗʰ Street, 5ᵗʰ Avenue**

c. Hospital: **5ᵗʰ Street, 2ⁿᵈ Avenue**

4. Add a square to the map to show the office tower, and add a triangle to show the theater. Identify where you put each.

a. Office tower: (_____ , _____)

b. Theater: (_____ , _____)

Check students' work.

page CC 63

Name _____

Common Core Standards Practice

5.G.3 Understand that attributes belonging to a category of two-dimensional figures also belong to all subcategories of that category.

1. What properties do isosceles and equilateral triangles share?

Answers may vary. Sample: They each have three angles and three sides. They each have two sides that are equal in length.

2. What properties do rhombuses and parallelograms share?

Answers may vary. Sample: They each are quadrilaterals. They each have two pairs of parallel sides.

3. Here are a rectangle, a square, and a rhombus.

a. What are the common properties of the rectangle and the square?

two pairs of parallel sides, all four angles are right angles

b. What are the common properties of the square and the rhombus?

two pairs of parallel sides, all four sides are equal in length

c. Of the three figures, which could also be classified as either of the other two figures? Explain.

The square; it is a rectangle because it has four right angles, and it is a rhombus because it has four sides of equal length.

page CC 64

4. Name a common property of trapezoids and quadrilaterals.

They each have four sides.

5. Put check marks in the table to show each figure that has the given property.

Property	Quadrilateral	Parallelogram	Trapezoid	Rectangle	Rhombus	Square
This figure has four sides.	✔	✔	✔	✔	✔	✔
This figure always has two pairs of parallel sides.		✔		✔	✔	✔
This figure has only one pair of parallel sides.			✔			
This figure always has four right angles.				✔		✔
This figure always has four sides of equal length.					✔	✔

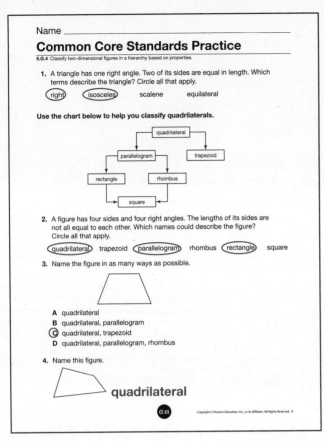

Name _____

Common Core Standards Practice

5.G.4 Classify two-dimensional figures in a hierarchy based on properties.

1. A triangle has one right angle. Two of its sides are equal in length. Which terms describe the triangle? Circle all that apply.

   (right)   (isosceles)   scalene   equilateral

Use the chart below to help you classify quadrilaterals.

```
              quadrilateral
              /          \
      parallelogram      trapezoid
       /        \
  rectangle    rhombus
       \        /
        square
```

2. A figure has four sides and four right angles. The lengths of its sides are not all equal to each other. Which names could describe the figure? Circle all that apply.

   (quadrilateral)   trapezoid   (parallelogram)   rhombus   (rectangle)   square

3. Name the figure in as many ways as possible.

   A quadrilateral
   B quadrilateral, parallelogram
   (C) quadrilateral, trapezoid
   D quadrilateral, parallelogram, rhombus

4. Name this figure.

   quadrilateral

page CC 65

---

5. Name this figure in as many ways as possible.

   ## quadrilateral, parallelogram, rectangle

6. Select the most specific classification for a figure that has four sides of equal length, but not four angles of equal measure.

   A quadrilateral
   B parallelogram
   (C) rhombus
   D trapezoid

7. What is the most specific classification for this figure?

   A quadrilateral   (C) trapezoid
   B parallelogram   D rhombus

8. Why are all rectangles examples of parallelograms, but all parallelograms are not rectangles?

   All rectangles have two pairs of parallel sides, which makes them parallelograms. However, many parallelograms have angles that are not right angles, so they are not rectangles.

9. Circle the statements that are true.

   (All squares are rectangles.)

   All rhombuses are squares.

   All quadrilaterals are trapezoids.

   (All rhombuses are parallelograms.)

   (All parellograms are quadrilaterals.)

page CC 66

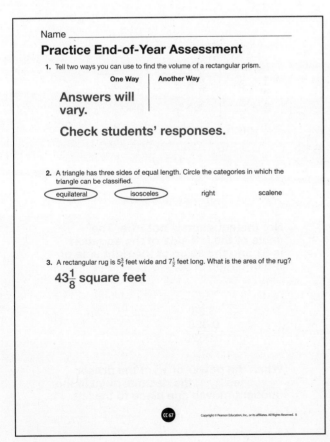

Name _____

Practice End-of-Year Assessment

1. Tell two ways you can use to find the volume of a rectangular prism.

One Way	Another Way

   Answers will vary.

   Check students' responses.

2. A triangle has three sides of equal length. Circle the categories in which the triangle can be classified.

   (equilateral)   (isosceles)   right   scalene

3. A rectangular rug is $5\frac{3}{4}$ feet wide and $7\frac{1}{2}$ feet long. What is the area of the rug?

   $43\frac{1}{8}$ **square feet**

page CC 67

---

4. To make a lace border for a hat, Rebecca uses $\frac{5}{12}$ yard of red lace and $\frac{1}{6}$ yard of green lace.

   a. Model the problem with this circle.

   b. How much lace does Rebecca use to make her hat?

   $\frac{7}{12}$ **yard**

5. Cassie's cat weighs $3\frac{1}{2}$ pounds. Her dog weighs 4 times as much as her cat. How much does her dog weigh?

   $3\frac{1}{2} \times 4 = 14$ **pounds**

6. Which describes the relationship between 15,700 and 157,000?

   (A) 15,700 is $\frac{1}{10}$ of 157,000.
   B 157,000 is $\frac{1}{10}$ of 15,700.
   C 15,700 is $\frac{1}{100}$ of 157,000.
   D 157,000 is $\frac{1}{100}$ of 15,700.

7. Find the quotient.

   $1,633 \div 23$.

   71

page CC 68

8. The line plot shows the birth weights, in pounds, of a litter of 8 puppies.

a. What is the difference in weight between the heaviest and lightest puppy?

$$\frac{6}{8} - \frac{2}{8} = \frac{4}{8} \text{ or } \frac{1}{2} \text{ pound}$$

b. Which birth weight was most common among the puppies?

$$\frac{1}{2} \text{ pound}$$

9. How is the value of 3 in the number 43,442 different from the value of 3 in the number 44,432?

The 3 in 43,442 represents 3 thousands, the 3 in 44,432 represents 3 tens. The 3 in 43,442 is 100 times the value of the 3 in 44,432.

10. Which model matches the division expression?

$3 \div 4$

A

B

C

Ⓓ

page CC 69

---

11. Label the x-axis, y-axis, and origin on the coordinate grid shown below. Use the letter "O" for the origin.

12. Match these numbers with their expanded forms.

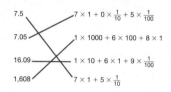

7.5

7.05

16.09

1,608

$7 \times 1 + 0 \times \frac{1}{10} + 5 \times \frac{1}{100}$

$1 \times 1000 + 6 \times 100 + 8 \times 1$

$1 \times 10 + 6 \times 1 + 9 \times \frac{1}{100}$

$7 \times 1 + 5 \times \frac{1}{10}$

13. Divide.

$0.84 \div 0.07$

12

14. Which of these numbers, when rounded to the nearest tenth, is 0.8? Circle all that round to 0.8.

Ⓐ0.76   Ⓑ0.84   0.72   0.079   Ⓒ0.79

page CC 70

---

15. Look at the following pairs of values.

x	y
1	5
2	8
3	11
4	14
5	17

a. What is the rule for each column?

The rule for the x column is Add 1; the rule for the y column is Add 3.

b. Write two more pairs of values that could be added to this table.

6	20
7	23

c. Graph these pairs of values on the coordinate grid. What do you notice about the graph of these values?

The values, when connected, form a line.

16. Dao has a cookie recipe that calls for $3\frac{1}{4}$ cups of flour. He plans to make $1\frac{1}{2}$ batches of cookies. Explain whether Dao will need more flour, less flour, or the same amount of flour as his recipe calls for.

Dao will need more flour than his recipe calls for since he is multiplying by a number larger than 1.

page CC 71

---

17. Write the expressions in the appropriate place. You should NOT find the products of the expressions.

Less than 3	Equal to 3	Greater than 3
$\frac{1}{3} \times 3$	$\frac{6}{6} \times 3$	$\frac{7}{6} \times 3$
$3 \times \frac{2}{5}$	$3 \times \frac{7}{7}$	$3 \times \frac{3}{2}$
$\frac{1}{4} \times 6$		$3 \times \frac{9}{7}$

$\frac{1}{3} \times 3$ $\frac{6}{6} \times 3$ $\frac{7}{6} \times 3$ $3 \times \frac{7}{7}$

$3 \times \frac{3}{2}$ $3 \times \frac{2}{5}$ $3 \times \frac{9}{7}$ $\frac{1}{4} \times 6$

18. Tell whether the equation is true. Justify your answer.

$36 - (12 + 8) \div 4 \overset{?}{=} 36 - 12 + 8 \div 4$

No, the equation is not true. The value of the left side of the equation is 31 and the value of the right side of the equation is 26.

19. Complete the table.

$32.8 \div 1$	32.8
$32.8 \div 10$	**3.28**
$32.8 \div 100$	**0.328**
$32.8 \div 1,000$	**0.0328**

Describe the pattern in the table.

When the power of 10 of the divisor increases by 1, the decimal point in the quotient moves one place to the left.

page CC 72

20. The length of a rectangular window is $5\frac{3}{4}$ feet and its width is $3\frac{1}{2}$ feet. What is the area of the window?

$20\frac{1}{8}$ ft²

21. Plot points M and L on the coordinate grid.

   a. Point M: (7, 3)

   b. Point L: (3, 1)

22. Paula covers her bathroom with pink and white tiles. Each tile is the same size. She uses $2\frac{1}{2}$ times more pink tiles than white tiles, and the white tiles cover $4\frac{1}{2}$ square feet. How much area do the pink tiles cover?

$4\frac{1}{2} \times 2\frac{1}{2} = 11\frac{1}{4}$ square feet

23. A concert hall has 2,312 seats. For one concert, each seat is sold for $89. What is the total amount of money in ticket sales if the concert is sold out?

2,312 × $89 = $205,768

page CC 73

---

24. A recipe calls for $\frac{2}{3}$ cup of brown sugar to make one batch of muffins. Amanda plans to make $5\frac{1}{2}$ batches of muffins.

   a. Draw a model to match the problem situation.

Check students' models

   b. How much brown sugar will Amanda need?

$3\frac{2}{3}$ cups

25. Find the product of 1,275 and 23,452.

29,901,300

26. Which of these are equal to the sum of $\frac{4}{12}$ and $\frac{6}{8}$? Circle all that are equal to the sum.

$\frac{10}{20}$ $\boxed{\frac{26}{24}}$ $\frac{10}{12}$ $\boxed{\frac{13}{12}}$ $\boxed{1\frac{1}{12}}$ $1\frac{2}{12}$

27. Mary studied math for $1\frac{1}{2}$ hours and science for $\frac{3}{5}$ hour. How many hours did she spend studying?

$2\frac{1}{10}$ hours

page CC 74

---

28. Which expression matches this statement?
four times the difference of 12 and 2

   A $4 + 12 - 2$

   B $12 - 2 \times 4$

   Ⓒ $4 \times (12 - 2)$

   D $4 \times 12 - 2$

29. A dolphin ate 2,604 pounds of fish during the 31 days of March.

   a. What is the average amount of fish the dolphin ate per day?

$2,604 \div 31 = 84$ pounds

   b. Draw a model to justify your answer.

Check students' models.

30. Pineapples cost $2.19 each. Watermelons cost $2.91 each.

   a. Which costs more: a pineapple or a watermelon?

a watermelon

   b. Write a number sentence to compare the two prices.

$2.19 < $2.91

page CC 75

---

31. A group of 6 friends wants to share 8 pears evenly. All of the pears are the same size.

   a. How many pears should each friend receive?

$\frac{4}{3}$ or $1\frac{1}{3}$ pears

   b. Explain how the friends should cut the pears and divide them.

Two pears should be cut into thirds. Each friend takes 1 whole pear and a one-third slice of a pear.

32. Drake has a piece of blue ribbon that is $\frac{1}{8}$ yard long, and a silver ribbon that is $\frac{3}{4}$ yard long. How much longer is the silver ribbon?

$\frac{5}{8}$ yard

33. Amy has 6 cups of applesauce. She divides the applesauce into $\frac{1}{2}$-cup servings.

   a. Draw a model to match the problem.

Check students' models.

   b. How many servings of applesauce does she have?

12 servings

34. A sporting goods factory produces 13,234 tennis balls per month. How many tennis balls does it produce during 12 months?

13,234 × 12 = 158,808

page CC 76

35. Emilio builds a flower planter in the shape of a rectangular prism. It is 4 feet long, 2 feet high, and 2 feet wide. What is the volume of the planter?

16 cubic feet

36. Four friends share $\frac{1}{4}$ of a cake. What fraction of the whole cake does each friend get?

$$\frac{1}{4} \div 4 = \frac{1}{16}$$

37. Which term could describe each of these three figures?

A square
B rhombus
C rectangle
Ⓓ parallelogram

page CC 77

38. Which of these are equal to the difference of $\frac{4}{6}$ and $\frac{2}{9}$? Circle all that are equal to the difference.

$\frac{1}{9}$ ⊘$\frac{4}{9}$ $\frac{2}{3}$ ⊘$\frac{8}{16}$ $\frac{3}{6}$ $\frac{8}{9}$

39. Find the volume of the rectangular prism shown below.

8 cm   6 cm   11 cm

528 cubic cm

40. Multiply.

9.3×4.27

39.711

41. Draw a model to find the product of $\frac{3}{8} \times 4$. Then find the product.

$$1\frac{1}{2}$$

page CC 78

42. What is 17.264 rounded to the nearest hundredth?

Ⓐ 17.26
B 17.27
C 17.3
D 17.24

43. Bargain Toys packs 1,440 toys onto 40 shelves. Each shelf holds the same number of toys. How many toys are on each shelf?

36 toys

44. Circle all of the expressions that equal 1,483,000.

1.483×10^{6} 14.83×10^{6} 148.3×10^{4}

148.3×10^{3} 1.483×10^{7} 14.83×10^{5}

45. Mr. Lee's fence is 10 yards long. How many feet long is the fence?

1 yard = 3 feet; 10 yards = 10 × 3 feet = 30 feet

page CC 79

Name _____

Performance Task 1
Storage Needs

Part A

Erica makes and sells homemade salad dressings. She packages the dressings in small jars, which she then places in boxes that hold 6 jars. The dimensions of the shipping boxes are 1 foot by 1 foot by 1 foot.

Erica has two different storage spaces for the boxes. One of the spaces is 4 feet long by 3 wide feet by 6 feet high. The other space measures 5 feet long by 3 feet wide by 5 feet high.

1. Into which storage area can Erica fit more boxes of dressing? How many more boxes can she fit into the larger area? Explain your answer with models.

The second storage space, which is 5 × 3 × 5 holds 3 more boxes of dressing. Each box is one cubic foot; the second storage area is 75 cubic feet, so it holds 75 boxes. The first area is 72 cubic feet so it holds 72 boxes. Check students' models.

page CC 80

Part B

Erica would like to increase the production of her salad dressings. To do so, she will need more storage space for boxes of jars. Erica has two options for additional storage space. Storage space C is 4 feet long by 6 feet wide by 6 feet high and storage space D is 8 feet long by 4 feet wide by 5 feet high. Including her original storage area, Erica would like to have a total of at least 280 cubic feet, but no more than 300 cubic feet, of storage space.

2. Which of the two additional storage space options should Erica choose? Explain your reasoning for the option you selected.

Erica currently has 147 cubic feet of storage space, so she is looking for no more than 153 cubic feet more. Storage space C is 144 cubic feet and storage space D is 160 cubic feet with storage space C, Erica would have 291 cubic feet of storage capacity and with storage space D, she would have 307 cubic feet, which is more than what she is looking for. She should choose storage space C.

page CC 81

Performance Task 2
Town Beautification

Part A

The Town Council in Center City will start a tree-planting program to beautify parts of the town. The plan calls for planting 2,000 trees. Below are three types of trees that have been recommended and are available for planting:

Type of Tree	Cost per Tree (including tax)
Cherry	$40.50
Dogwood	$65.00
Myrtle	$50.50

The Town Council voted to budget $100,000 to buy the 2,000 trees. Both the Parks Department, which will purchase and plant the trees, and the Town Council, agree that there should be a mix of all three types of trees.

The towns people were also surveyed about which types of trees to plant. The result of the survey show that cherry trees are a town favorite, so the Town Council has recommended that at least half of the trees planted by cherry trees.

1. You have been asked by the Parks Department to determine how many of each type of tree the Parks Department should purchase and the total cost. In your proposal, you should come as close as you can to spending all of the money budgeted for the purchase of the trees. You need to answer these questions in your proposal:

   a. What is the total number of each type of tree to be planted?

   b. What is the total amount needed to purchase each type of tree?

   c. What is the total amount needed to purchase all types of trees?

   The Town Council wants half of the trees to be cherry trees, so that means that $40,500 will be spend on cherry trees. That leaves $59,500 for 1,000 trees. 620 dogwood and 380 myrtle trees would cost $40,300 + 19,190 = 59,490 for a total of $99,990. (acceptable answers: 600 cherry and 400 myrtle)

page CC 82

Part B

The Parks Department will be responsible for planting all of the trees for the tree-planting program. According to the tree nursery, each newly planted tree will need a layer of organic mulch. The nursery estimates that each cherry tree planted will require 20 pounds of mulch, each dogwood tree 25 pounds of mulch, and each myrtle tree 20 pounds of mulch. The nursery sells mulch for $34.95 a ton. It does not sell fractions of a ton.

2. How much money will the Parks Department need in order to purchase mulch for all of the trees in your proposal?

For the 1000 cherry trees, 20,000 pounds of mulch is needed. For the 620 dogwood trees, 15,500 pounds of mulch is needed and for the 380 myrtle trees, 7600 pounds of mulch is needed. That gives a total of 43,100 pounds of mulch, or 21.55 tons. Since mulch is sold only by the ton, the Parks Department will need 22 tons of mulch for a total cost of $768.90.

page CC 83

Name _____

Practice End-of-Year Assessment
Test 2

1. Small cubes were joined together to form a larger cube, as shown below.

a. Explain how to find the volume of the large cube.

Check students' explanations.

b. What is the volume of the large cube?

27 cubic units

2. Circle the categories in which this figure can be classified.

4 cm
4 cm

(quadrilateral) (square) (rhombus) (parallelogram) (rectangle)

3. A rectangular painting is $1\frac{2}{3}$ feet long and $1\frac{1}{2}$ feet high. What is the area of the painting?

$2\frac{1}{2}$ square feet

page CC 85

---

4. Sarah and Ann are painting a wall in Ann's bedroom. On the first day, Sarah paints $\frac{1}{4}$ of the wall, and Ann paints $\frac{1}{3}$ of the wall.

a. Model the problem with this square.

Check students' models.

b. How much of the wall is left to paint?

$\frac{5}{12}$

5. Kento's recipe for a batch of muffins calls for $2\frac{1}{2}$ cups of flour. How much flour would Kento need to make $3\frac{1}{2}$ batches of muffins?

$8\frac{3}{4}$ cups

6. Which describes the relationship between 70,070 and 7,007?

A 70,070 is 10 times 7,007.

B 70,070 is 100 times 7,007.

C 70,070 is $\frac{1}{10}$ of 7,007.

D 70,070 is $\frac{1}{100}$ of 7,007.

7. Find the quotient.

9,888 ÷ 16

618

page CC 86

---

8. Chan walks dogs every afternoon. The table shows the amount of time he walked dogs each day during the past week.

Time Spent Walking Dogs (hours)						
$\frac{1}{2}$	$\frac{3}{4}$	$\frac{1}{4}$	$\frac{1}{2}$	$\frac{3}{4}$	$\frac{1}{2}$	$\frac{1}{4}$

a. Make a line plot of the data.

Check students' graphs.

Time Spent Walking Dogs

b. What was the most common time spent walking dogs?

$\frac{1}{2}$ hour

c. What was the greatest difference in time spent walking dogs?

$\frac{1}{2}$ hour

9. A five-digit number is made from the digits 6, 6, 3, 3, and 3. Write two numbers in which the places of the two 6's are separated by a factor of 1,000?

63,363 and 36,336

10. Which model matches the division expression?

4 ÷ 6

A

Ⓑ

C

D

page CC 87

---

11. On the coordinate grid, what is the name of the point where the x-axis meets the y-axis?

the origin

12. Match these numbers with their expanded forms.

70.6

7.06

14.3

1403

$1 \times 1000 + 4 \times 100 + 3 \times 1$

$7 \times 100 + 6 \times \frac{1}{10}$

$7 \times 1 + 6 \times \frac{1}{100}$

$1 \times 10 + 4 \times 1 + 3 \times \frac{1}{10}$

13. Find the quotient.

3.84 ÷ 0.96

4

14. Which of these numbers, when rounded to the nearest hundredth, is 0.56? Circle all that round to 0.56.

0.566   (0.556)   (0.563)   0.554   (0.555)   (0.565)

page CC 88

15. Look at the following pairs of values.

x	y
1	2
2	4
3	6
4	8
5	10

a. What is the rule for each column?

The rule for the x column is Add 1; the rule for the y column is Add 3.

b. Write two more pairs of values that could be added to this table.

6	12
7	14

c. Graph these pairs of values on the coordinate grid. What do you notice about the graph of these values? **The values, when connected, form a line.**

16. Fred cuts a 12-inch piece of rope. Then he cuts a second piece of rope that is $\frac{3}{2}$ longer than the first piece. Is the second piece shorter or longer than the first piece? Explain how you know.

The second piece is longer because $\frac{3}{2}$ is greater than 1.

page CC 89

17. Write the expressions in the appropriate place. You should NOT find the products of the expressions.

Less than 5	Equal to 5	Greater than 5
$\frac{2}{5} \times 5$	$5 \times \frac{3}{3}$	$\frac{3}{2} \times 5$
$5 \times \frac{2}{3}$	$\frac{4}{4} \times 5$	$5 \times \frac{8}{5}$
$\frac{3}{4} \times 5$		$5 \times \frac{5}{3}$

$5 \times \frac{2}{3}$ $\frac{3}{4} \times 5$ $5 \times \frac{3}{3}$ $\frac{4}{4} \times 5$

$5 \times \frac{5}{3}$ $\frac{3}{2} \times 5$ $5 \times \frac{8}{5}$ $\frac{2}{5} \times 5$

18. Tell whether the equation is true. Justify your answer.
$24 \times 3 + (15 - 7) \div 2 \stackrel{?}{=} 8 \times 9 + 12 \div 2$

No, the equation is not true. The value of the left side of the equation is 76 and the value of the right side of the equation is 78.

19. Complete the table.

$72.4 \div 1$	**72.4**
$72.4 \div 10^1$	**7.24**
$72.4 \div 10^2$	**0.724**
$72.4 \div 10^3$	**0.0724**

Describe the pattern in the table.

When the power of 10 of the divisor increases by 1, the decimal point in the quotient moves one place to the left.

page CC 90

20. The dimensions of a rectangular photo frame are $4\frac{1}{3}$ in. by $3\frac{1}{3}$ in. What is the area of the photo frame?

$14\frac{4}{9}$ sq in.

21. Write the coordinates of each animal picture on the coordinate grid.

a. Zebra   **(8, 8)**   **d.** Elephant   **(4, 7)**

b. Alligator   **(9, 2)**   **e.** Panda   **(1, 9)**

c. Tiger   **(6, 5)**   **f.** Giraffe   **(2, 4)**

22. Lee can sew $3\frac{3}{4}$ sock monkeys in one hour. How many sock monkeys can he sew in $6\frac{1}{2}$ hours of work?

$6\frac{1}{2} \times 3\frac{3}{4} = 24\frac{3}{8}$ sock monkeys

23. Find the product of 2,212 and 95.

$2212 \times 95 = 210,140$

page CC 91

24. A recipe calls for $\frac{3}{4}$ cup of tomato sauce to make one batch of spaghetti sauce. Freddie plans to make $3\frac{1}{2}$ batches of spaghetti sauce.

a. Draw a model to match the problem situation.

Check students' models.

b. How much tomato sauce will Freddie need?

$2\frac{5}{8}$ cups

25. Find the product of 1,012 and 45,124.

45,665,488

26. Which of these are equal to the sum of $\frac{7}{12} + \frac{7}{8}$? Circle all that are equal to the sum.

$\frac{14}{20}$ $\frac{35}{24}$ $\frac{14}{12}$

$\frac{17}{12}$ $1\frac{11}{24}$ $1\frac{5}{12}$

27. To make trail mix, Andre adds $\frac{3}{5}$ cup of peanuts and $\frac{2}{3}$ cut of walnuts. How many cups of nuts are in the trail mix?

$1\frac{4}{15}$ cups

page CC 92

28. Which expression matches this statement?

45 is divided by the sum of 9 and 6.

A $45 \div 9 + 6$

B $(45 \div 9) + 6$

C $45 \div (9 + 6)$

D $45 + 9 \div 6$

29. The Tran family drove 1,246 miles during a vacation that lasted 14 days.

a. How many miles on average did they drive each day?

1,246 ÷ 14 = 89 miles

b. Draw a model to justify your answer.

Check students' drawings.

30. In a track and field event, the times of the top three finishers were 9.85 seconds, 9.9 seconds, and 9.82 seconds.

a. Order the times from least to greatest.

9.82, 9.85, 9.9

b. Write a number sentence to compare the three times.

9.9 > 9.85 > 9.82

page CC 93

---

31. A group of 5 friends bakes 8 pies. All of the pies are the same size. The 5 friends will share the pies equally.

a. How much pie should each friend receive?

$$\frac{8}{5} = 1\frac{3}{5} \text{ pies}$$

b. Explain how the friends could share the pies.

Check students' answers

32. During a movie, Russell ate $\frac{4}{5}$ of a bucket of popcorn and Jack ate $\frac{3}{4}$ of a bucket of popcorn. How much more popcorn did Russell eat?

$$\frac{1}{20} \text{ bucket}$$

33. James has 4 apples. He slices each apple into quarters.

a. Draw a model to match the problem.

Check students' models.

b. How many $\frac{1}{4}$-apple slices does he have?

16 slices

34. Pop's Pizza makes an average of 11,234 pizzas per month. How many pizzas do they make in a year?

134,808 pizzas

page CC 94

---

35. Hanh is looking at a fish aquarium. It is in the shape of a rectangular prism that is 2 feet wide, 5 feet long, and 2 feet tall. What is the volume of the fish tank?

20 cubic feet

36. Anna's mother baked a plum cake and gave $\frac{1}{2}$ of it to Anna. Anna divided the piece equally among 6 friends. What fraction of the whole cake did each friend get?

$$\frac{1}{12} \text{ of the whole cake}$$

37. Which term best describes these three figures?

A irregular polygons

B regular polygons

C quadrilaterals

D hexagons

page CC 95

---

38. Which of these are equal to the difference of $\frac{1}{3}$ and $\frac{1}{7}$? Circle all that are equal to the difference.

$\frac{2}{10}$ $\frac{10}{21}$ $\boxed{\frac{4}{21}}$ $\frac{2}{3}$ $\frac{0}{4}$ $\frac{4}{10}$

39. Find the volume of the rectangular prism shown below.

8 cm   14 cm   8 cm

896 cubic cm

40. Multiply.

2.62×3.5

9.17

41. Draw a model to find the product of $3 \times \frac{3}{4}$. Then find the product.

$$2\frac{1}{4}$$

page CC 96

42. What is 0.367 rounded to the nearest hundredth?

A 0.3
B 0.36
C 0.37
D 0.4

43. A local charity received 1,800 blankets. They distribute them equally to 36 local shelters. How many blankets will each shelter receive?

50 blankets

44. Which of these expressions are equivalent to 54,200,000? Circle all of the expressions.

5.42×10^7 5.42×10^6 54.2×10^6

542×10^5 54.2×10^7 5.42×10^8

45. The height of a room is 9 feet. What is the height in inches?

108 inches

page CC 97

Name _____

Performance Task 3
Arts and Crafts
Part A

Amanda and her mother decorate picture frames to sell at craft shows. They put decorative ribbon around the frames, with a one-inch overlap. On some frames they add a decorative bow, which requires an additional $3\frac{1}{2}$ inches of ribbon.

Amanda has 10 feet of striped ribbon. She wants to be able to decorate five frames, two small frames that are 4 in. by 6 in., one medium-sized frame that is 5 in. by 7 in.; and two large frames that are 8 in. by 10 in.

1. Does Amanda have enough ribbon to decorate the five frames? Justify your answer by showing how much ribbon she needs for each frame and the total amount of ribbon she would use. Use models or equations to support your answer.

   No, she doesn't have enough ribbon. She needs 141 inches of ribbon and she has only 10 feet, or 120 inches. She needs 21 inches for each small frame, 25 inches for each medium-sized frame, and 37 inches for the large frames. Check students' explanations. Check that students have added the 1 inch overlap to the ribbon lengths for each frame.

2. If Amanda has enough ribbon, what could she do with the remaining ribbon? If she does not have enough ribbon, how should she adjust her plans to maximize ribbon use?

   Check students' answers. Students should acknowledge that she doesn't have enough ribbon, so she will need to adjust her plans. Possible options: decorate only one small frame (exactly 120 inches), do not decorate a medium-sized frame and use the remaining 4 inches to make a bow for one of the frames ($119\frac{1}{2}$ inches); decorate only one large frame and use the remaining 16 inches to make 4 bows (118 inches).

page CC 98

Part B

Amanda and her mother have these frames to sell at the craft fair. They plan to sell the 4 in. × 6 in. frames for $5, the 5 in. × 7 in. frames for $8, and the 8 in. × 10 in. frames for $10. They charge an extra dollar for frames with a bow.

Frame Size	Number
4 in. × 6 in. with bow	5
4 in. × 6 in. without bow	5
5 in. × 7 in. with bow	4
5 in. × 7 in. without bow	6
8 in. × 10 in. with bow	5
8 in. × 10 in. without bow	3

3. They would like to make $150 from selling frames at the craft fair. Will they be able to achieve their goal? If yes, explain how you know. Then describe one way that they can make $150. If not, explain why it is not possible.

   Yes, they can achieve their goal because they have $224 worth of frames for sale. Check students' descriptions of what Amanda and her mother could sell to reach their goal. Possible option: selling all of the small and medium-sized frames and at least 1 large frame.

4. If Amanda and her mother decide to add a bow to all of the frames before selling them, how should they price the frames so that they can make at least $300 if they sell all of their frames?

   Check students' explanations. Possible option: they can sell small frames for $8; medium-sized frames for $11, and large frames for $14; total $302.

page CC 99

Name _____

Performance Task 4
Yogurt Containers
Part A

Amy's family owns a frozen yogurt business. They have small yogurt cups that hold $\frac{1}{2}$ cup of frozen yogurt and medium cups that hold $\frac{3}{4}$ cup of frozen yogurt. The table below shows the number of cups sold in one day.

Cup Size	Number of Cups Sold
small	28
medium	16

1. Amy's family made 5 gallons of frozen yogurt. How many days will it take before they run out of frozen yogurt? (Assume that the data in the table is representative of daily sales.)

   They will have enough for three days, but will run out of yogurt early on the fourth day.

2. They make frozen yogurt in batches that are 5 gallons each. How many batches of frozen yogurt will they need to make to have enough for one week?

   A 5-gallon batch will last 3 days, so in one week they will need three batches, but in the following week, they might need to make only two batches.

page CC 100

Part B

The table from Part A showed the sales on a weekday when school was in session. Amy's family sells $1\frac{1}{2}$ times as much frozen yogurt on a weekday when school is not in session. They sell $2\frac{1}{4}$ times as much frozen yogurt on weekend days.

3. How much yogurt do you think Amy's family will need to make for one week when school is in session?

   For one week while school is in session, her family will need to make 247 cups of frozen yogurt or just over 15 gallons, so they would need to make four 5-gallon batches to have enough in one week, but they would only need to make three 5-gallon batches on some weeks.

4. How much frozen yogurt do you think Amy's family should make each week when school is not in session?

   For one week while school is not in session, her family will need to make 312 cups of frozen yogurt or 19.5 gallons, so they would need to make four 5-gallon batches to have enough each week.

5. What other factors might Amy's family want to consider when deciding how much frozen yogurt to make each week?

   Check students' answers. Sample: They might sell less frozen yogurt when it is cold outside. They might want to know how much of each flavor to make.

page CC 101

Practice End-of-Year Assessments Correlation Chart

Test 1 and Test 2

The chart below provides information about the two Practice End-of-Year Assessments, Test 1, found in the students' workbook and Test 2, a secure version, found in this Teacher's Guide, starting on page CC 85. The chart lists the Standard for Mathematical Content that is the primary assessment focus of each item. It also indicates whether the standard assessed is a major, supporting or additional content emphasis (as determined by both PARCC and SBAC). Finally, the last column points to the lesson(s) in enVisionMATH Common Core where students can be directed if they need additional practice or review of concepts.

Item Test 1 and Test 2	CCSS	Content Emphasis	enVisionMATH Common Core Lessons	Investigations Units.
1	5.MD.3	Major	12-1	U2 Inv. 1
2	5.G.3	Additional	15-2	U5 Inv. 1
3	5.NF.4	Major	11-2, 11-4, 11-5, 11-6	U4 Inv. 4A
4	5.NF.2	Major	9-1, 9-2, 9-6, 9-7	U4 Inv. 3
5	5.NF.6	Major	11-8	U4 Inv. 4A
6	5.NBT.1	Major	1-1	U3 Inv. 1
7	5.NBT.6	Major	5-2, 5-6, 5-7	U1 Inv. 3; U7 Inv. 3
8	5.MD.2	Supporting	14-1, 14-3	U9 Inv. 1
9	5.NBT.1	Major	1-1	U3 Inv. 1
10	5.NF.3	Major	11-1	U6 Inv. 1
11	5.G.1	Additional	16-1	U8 Inv. 1
12	5.NBT.3	Major	1-1, 1-2, 1-3, 1-4	U6 Inv. 1; U6 Inv. 3A
13	5.NBT.7	Major	7-6	U6 Inv. 3A
14	5.NBT.4	Major	2-2	U6 Inv. 3A
15	5.OA.3	Additional	8-5, 8-7	U8 Inv. 1; U8 Inv. 2
16	5.NF.5	Major	11-3, 11-7	U4 Inv. 4A
17	5.NF.5	Major	11-3, 11-7	U4 Inv. 4A
18	5.OA.1	Additional	8-2, 8-3, 8-4	U1 Inv. 1
19	5.NBT.2	Major	7-1	U6 Inv. 3A
20	5.NF.4	Major	11-3, 11-4, 11-5	U4 Inv. 4A

Item Test 1 and Test 2	CCSS	Content Emphasis	enVisionMATH Common Core Lessons	Investigations Units.
21	5.G.2	Additional	16-4, 16-5	U8 Inv. 1; U8 Inv. 2
22	5.NF.6	Major	11-3, 11-4, 11-5, 11-8	U4 Inv. 4A
23	5.NBT.5	Major	3-3, 3-5, 3-7, 3-8	U1 Inv. 2; U7 Inv. 2
24	5.NF.6	Major	11-8	U4 Inv. 4A
25	5.NBT.5	Major	3-3, 3-8	U1 Inv. 2; U7 Inv. 2
26	5.NF.1	Major	9-1, 9-2, 9-7	U4 Inv. 1; U4 Inv. 3
27	5.NF.2	Major	10-2, 10-4	U4 Inv. 3
28	5.OA.2	Additional	8-1	U1 Inv. 1; U7 Inv. 1
29	5.NBT.6	Major	5-2, 5-3, 5-6, 5-7	U1 Inv. 3; U7 Inv. 3
30	5.NBT.3	Major	1-6	U6 Inv. 1
31	5.NF.3	Major	11-1	U6 Inv. 1
32	5.NF.2	Major	9-1, 9-8	U4 Inv. 3
33	5.NF.7	Major	11-9	U4 Inv. 4A
34	5.NBT.5	Major	3-3, 3-8	U1 Inv. 2; U7 Inv. 2
35	5.MD.5	Major	12-5	U2 Inv. 1; U2 Inv. 2
36	5.NF.7	Major	11-10	U4 Inv. 4A
37	5.G.4	Additional	15-1, 15-3	U5 Inv. 1
38	5.NF.1	Major	9-1, 9-2, 9-8	U4 Inv. 1; U4 Inv. 3
39	5.MD.5	Major	12-3, 12-5	U2 Inv. 1; U2 Inv. 2
40	5.NBT.7	Major	6-3, 6-6	U6 Inv. 2; U6 Inv. 3A
41	5.NF.4	Major	11-2	U4 Inv. 4A
42	5.NBT.4	Major	2-2	U6 Inv. 3A
43	5.NBT.6	Major	5-4, 5-6, 5-7	U1 Inv. 3; U7 Inv. 3
44	5.NBT.2	Major	6-1	U6 Inv. 3A
45	5.MD.1	Supporting	13-1	U8 Inv. 1

Performance Tasks Scoring Rubrics

Performance Task 1 – Storage Needs

Primary Content Domains and Clusters

Measurement and Data: Geometric measurement: understand concepts of volume and relate volume to multiplication and to addition. (5.MD.3, 5.MD.4, 5.MD.5)

Secondary Content Domains and Clusters

Number and Operations in Base Ten: Perform operations with multi-digit whole numbers and decimals to the hundredths. (5.NBT.5); Generalize place value understanding for multi-digit whole numbers. (4.NBT.2)

Math Practices Focus

MP 1, 2, 4, 6, 7

Scoring Rubric

1	Determines into which storage area more boxes can fit.	10
	Calculates the volume of both spaces.	
	Calculates the difference between the two volumes.	
	Identifies the space with the greater volume.	
	Determines the number of boxes that can fit into both areas.	
	Explains answers using models of the two spaces.	
2	Selects the appropriate storage space.	10
	Calculates the volume of both spaces.	
	Identifies the space that fits the criteria given.	
	Explains reasoning for selection.	
TOTAL		20

Performance Task 2 – Town Beautification

Primary Content Domains and Clusters

Number and Operations in Base Ten: Perform operations with multi-digit whole numbers and decimals to the hundredths. (5.NBT.5, 5.NBT.6, 5.NBT.7)

Math Practices Focus

MP 1, 2, 3, 4

Scoring Rubric

1	Presents a proposal that fits all criteria presented.	10
	Finds the cost of the cherry trees.	
	Determines an appropriate number of dogwood trees and myrtle trees that fits criteria presented.	
2	Calculate the cost for mulch for all the trees.	10
	Uses the number of trees of each type from part 1.	
	Calculates the amount of mulch needed accurately.	
	Calculates the cost of mulch needed accurately.	
TOTAL		20

Performance Task 3 – Arts and Crafts

Primary Content Domains and Clusters

Operations and Algebraic Thinking: Perform operations with multi-digit whole numbers and decimals to the hundredths. (5.NBT.5, 5.NBT.6)

Secondary Content Domains and Clusters

Measurement and Data: Convert like measurement units within a given measurement system. (5.MD.1)

Math Practices Focus

MP 1, 2, 4, 6, 7

Scoring Rubric

1	**Determines that Amanda does not have enough ribbon.**	6
	Calculates the amount of ribbon needed total.	
	Calculates the amount of ribbon needed for each type of frame.	
	Converts measure to compare lengths.	
2	**Proposes a viable alternate plan.**	4
	Identifies a correct number of each size that could be decorated.	
	Explains how the plans will differ.	
3	**Explains one way to make at least $150.**	5
	Describes one possible outcome with an income of at least $150.	
	Identifies that it is possible to make at least $150.	
4	**Explains one way to make at least $300.**	5
	Describes a pricing method that allows them to have an income of at least $300.	
	Identifies that prices must be increased on frames.	
TOTAL		**20**

Performance Task 4 – Yogurt Containers

Primary Content Domains and Clusters

Number and Operations – Fractions: Apply and extend previous understandings of multiplication and division to multiply and divide fractions. (5.NF.4, 5.NF.6)

Secondary Content Domains and Clusters

Measurement and Data: Convert like measurement units within a given measurement systems. (5.MD.1)

Math Practices Focus

MP 1, 2, 4, 6, 7, 8

Scoring Rubric

1	**Determines how long one batch will last at given rate.**	4
	Converts amounts from number sold to cups sold to gallons sold.	
	Calculates the number of days one batch will last.	
2	**Determines the correct number of batches needed.**	4
	Calculates using result from part 1 how many batches are needed for one week.	
3	**Determines the correct number of batches needed.**	5
	Calculates the amount of frozen yogurt needed using the table and the information given.	
	Uses results from parts 1 and 2 to find answer.	
4	**Determines the correct number of batches needed.**	5
	Calculates the amount of frozen yogurt needed using the table and the information given.	
	Uses results from parts 1 and 2 to find answer.	
5	**Identifies other factors on frozen yogurt sales.**	2
	Shows understanding of other factors that might affect sales besides day of the week and school being in session or not.	
TOTAL		20